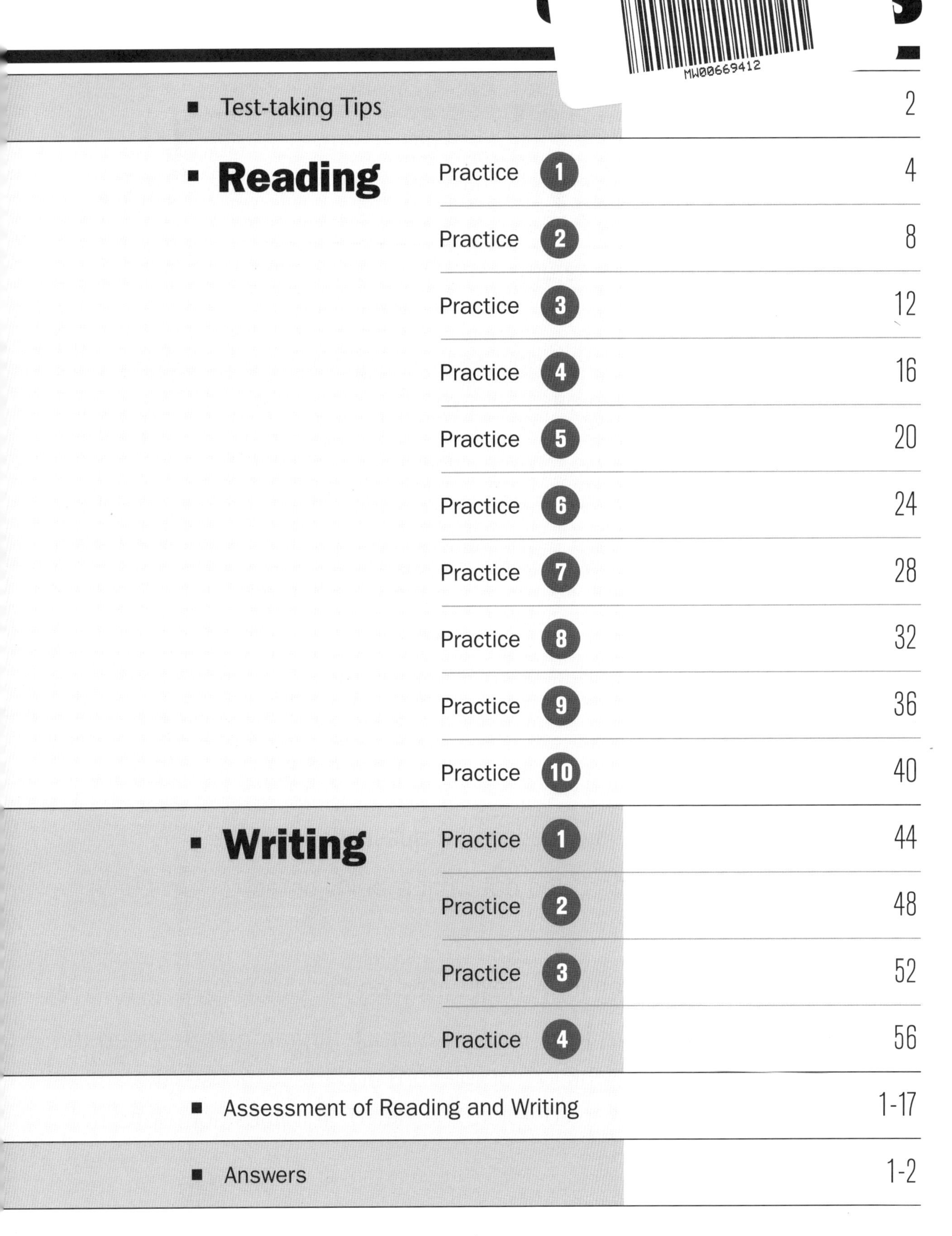

Printed in China

Test-taking TIPS

General

- Count the number of pages to make sure that there are no missing pages.
- Read the instructions carefully so that you know what to do and how to do it.
- In multiple-choice questions, read all the four options before deciding which is the correct answer.
- Write neatly.
- Always check your answers and writing after you have completed the test.

READING

- Read the text once before reading the questions.
- When reading a question, find out what is being asked.
- Look for clue words.
- Look for the information in the text based on the clue words.
- In multiple-choice questions, look for consistent grammar between the stem (the part with a blank for completion) and the response (the choice to be put into the blank to complete the stem). If it does not sound right, it is probably wrong.

- If you see "use information from the text and your own ideas", it means that you can use specific details from the reading selection and at the same time include your prior knowledge and experience of the topic in your answer.

WRITING

- Read the instruction carefully so that you know exactly what you are asked to write about.
- Pay attention to the key words such as "describe" and "explain".
- "Describe" means that you have to use words to tell the reader how something looks and feels. It is like using words to create a mental picture for the reader.
- "Explain" means you have to use words to make clear how something works or why something happens or works the way it does. You need to give supporting details step-by-step.
- Ask yourself the five "W-" and one "H-" questions to generate ideas for your writing. These question words are: who, what, when, why, where, and how.
- Jot down the ideas that come to your mind. Organize them and write a draft.
- After writing, check your spelling, grammar, and punctuation.

Sunflowers

The sunflower plant is a very attractive yellow flower. It gets its name from its yellow sun-like face and also from the ability to rotate its face toward the sun as the sun moves from east to west during the day. With plenty of sun and water, the sunflower can grow over three metres tall. 1

The sunflower is so beautiful that it is often used in flower arrangements. It has been painted by many artists, too. 2

Even the famous artist Vincent Van Gogh did a series of sunflower paintings. The sunflower design is often used in arts and crafts and even fabric for clothing.

3 However, the sunflower is more than a pretty yellow flower. It is an important farm crop and provides food for people and wildlife. Sunflower seeds are used as a snack food. Birds love sunflower seeds and many people buy black oil sunflower seeds for their bird feeders.

4 The most important use of the sunflower crop is for sunflower oil. Sunflower oil is extracted from sunflower seeds. It is used for salad dressings, frying, and baking.

5 So you can see that the sunflower is a beautiful plant and also an excellent source of food. It is a very important crop on prairie farms in Canada.

1

1. What kind of text is this piece of reading?

   - ○ a poem
   - ○ a story
   - ○ an article
   - ○ a piece of news

2. What is the first paragraph of the text mainly about?

   - ○ things that are special about the sunflower
   - ○ how the sunflower gets its name
   - ○ the size of the sunflower
   - ○ how the sunflower can grow tall

3. According to the text, which word shows that Vincent Van Gogh is well-known?

   - ○ series
   - ○ artist
   - ○ famous
   - ○ paintings

4. According to the text, which of the following statements is true?

   - ○ Sunflowers can turn to face the sun.
   - ○ Sunflowers are a snack food.
   - ○ Birds like to feed on sunflowers.
   - ○ Sunflowers are used for baking.

5 Read this sentence from paragraph 1.

The sunflower plant is a very attractive yellow flower.

Which word suggests that the author likes sunflowers?

- ○ very
- ○ attractive
- ○ yellow
- ○ flower

6 Read this sentence from paragraph 2.

The sunflower design is often used in arts and crafts and even fabric for clothing.

The word "fabric" means

- ○ drawing.
- ○ cloth.
- ○ weaving.
- ○ needlework.

7 According to the text, which of the following statements is NOT true?

- ○ Sunflowers are a farm crop.
- ○ People like using sunflowers in flower arrangements.
- ○ Sunflowers can grow to a height of over three metres.
- ○ Black oil sunflower seeds are good for making salad.

A Letter from Angela

35 Mountain Trail
Québec City, Quebec
February 12, 2008

Dear Aunt Polly,

Here we are in beautiful Mount St. Anne, Quebec. I can't believe that I have learned to ski in just one day! I thought it would be much harder and scarier than it was. 1

First, we booked lessons with our instructor and then we were fitted for boots, skis, and poles. It was difficult to walk in them, but with Dad's help, I managed to make it to meet our instructor, Jean-Luc. 2

Jean-Luc first taught me how to fall down and to stand back up again. We practised stopping by pointing the toes of our skis so that it looked like a slice of pizza. Then we were ready to go on the lift. 3

The view on the top of the hill was spectacular, but I was pretty nervous about how I would make it down the hill. Jean-Luc helped me get off the lift and took me over to the beginner hill. Together, we carefully made our way down the hill. I was having so much fun I didn't even notice that we were picking up speed. Before I knew it, we had reached the bottom and I was ready to try it all over again. 4

Mom and Dad were really impressed to see me ski. They took lots of pictures and clapped for me at the end of the day. I can hardly wait to go back tomorrow. 5

Maybe this time, I'll try a bigger hill. 6

Love,

Angela

2

1 Why does Angela end the following sentence with an exclamation mark?

I can't believe that I have learned to ski in just one day!

- o to show that she was surprised
- o to show that she wanted to learn more about skiing
- o to describe how good she was at skiing
- o to end the sentence with style

2 Read this part of the sentence from paragraph 2.

It was difficult to walk in them,

The word "them" refers to

- o snow.
- o boots.
- o boots and skis.
- o poles.

3 Read this sentence from paragraph 3.

We practised stopping by pointing the toes of our skis so that it looked like a slice of pizza.

In this sentence, the words "a slice of pizza" mean

- o an inverted V shape.
- o a W shape.
- o a Y shape.
- o a U shape.

4 Which of the following sentences from the letter shows that Angela was worried about her first ski downhill?

- ○ I thought it would be much harder and scarier than it was.
- ○ I was pretty nervous about how I would make it down the hill.
- ○ I managed to make it to meet our instructor, Jean-Luc.
- ○ Together, we carefully made our way down the hill.

5 Which of the following words best describes Angela's first skiing trip?

- ○ entertaining
- ○ exciting
- ○ joyful
- ○ impressive

6 Who were on the skiing trip?

- ○ Angela, Angela's parents, and Aunt Polly
- ○ Jean-Luc, Angela's parents, and Angela
- ○ Angela's mom and dad, Angela, and Aunt Polly
- ○ Angela, Aunt Polly, Jean-Luc

Making Tomato Sauce

Labour Day weekend is the most important time of the year for the Romano family. Every year on this weekend, the entire family gather together to make their supply of tomato sauce. They will make enough to last the whole year! They will give some to Grandpa and Grandma too. 1

It was no exception this year. Mrs. Romano was busy cleaning the huge stainless steel pots in which the tomatoes would be cooked. Mr. Romano was preparing the outdoor stove 2 which would be used to heat the pots. Their two daughters, Janet and Martha, had the job of washing the tomatoes.

3 Once the tomatoes were washed, the family sat down at the table and began to cut the tomatoes into chunks. The chunks were then placed into the pots. When they had filled one, Mr. and Mrs. Romano worked together to lift it onto the stove. The pot was slowly heated until the tomatoes started to boil. Mrs. Romano would then add some special ingredients to the tomatoes and stood by the stove stirring and watching them turn into a thick sauce.

4 When the tomato sauce was ready, one important thing had to be done. The sauce had to be tasted. Mrs. Romano boiled some pasta and topped it with freshly made sauce. She gave a bowl to each family member and together, they sampled the result of their hard work. After one taste, all four of the Romanos smiled, satisfied with what they had done. The tomato sauce was ready to be put into glass jars.

Yummy! Yummy!

3

1 Which of the following sentences shows that the Romano family makes tomato sauce every year?

- ○ Labour Day weekend is the most important time of the year for the Romano family.
- ○ It was no exception this year.
- ○ They will make enough to last the whole year!
- ○ They will give some to Grandpa and Grandma too.

2 Which of the following phrases shows that the tomato sauce was tasty?

- ○ freshly made sauce
- ○ ready to be put into glass jars
- ○ sampled the result of their hard work
- ○ satisfied with what they had done

3 According to the story, the Romano family was making tomato sauce

- ○ in the kitchen.
- ○ in the park.
- ○ outdoors.
- ○ indoors.

4 Read this sentence from paragraph 4.

She gave a bowl to each family member and together, they sampled the result of their hard work.

The word "sampled" means

- ○ examined.
- ○ tasted.
- ○ enjoyed.
- ○ tested.

5 Who did the actual cooking of the tomato sauce?

- ○ Mr. Romano
- ○ Mrs. Romano
- ○ Janet
- ○ Martha

6 Which of the following would be the best new title for the story?

- ○ How to Make Tomato Sauce
- ○ The Romanos' "Tomato Sauce" Day
- ○ A Labour Day Weekend
- ○ Homemade Tomato Sauce

The Food Chain

The simple garden shows how a food chain works. Suppose you have lettuce growing in your garden. That lettuce gets energy from sunlight. It also soaks up water and nutrients from the soil. It now has everything it needs to grow. Think of this lettuce as the first link in a garden food chain. 1

Suppose one night a slug slithers onto the leaf of the lettuce and begins eating it. The energy from the lettuce is now transferred to the slug. The slug becomes the second link in the food chain. 2

In the morning, a beetle comes along, sees the slug and eats it. The energy from the slug is now passed on to the beetle and the beetle becomes the third link in the chain.

Just then, along comes a hungry shrew that eats the beetle. Now the shrew is enjoying all the energy in the chain. But it is not over yet. A wise old owl happens to spot the shrew. It swoops down, picks up the shrew, and returns to its nest to prepare it for dinner. 3

The owl has no natural predators. That means there is no animal that tries to kill the owl for food. The owl is at the top of this food chain and benefits from all the energy passed through all the members of the chain – the lettuce, the slug, the beetle, and the shrew. 4

There are many different food chains in nature. Each environment has its own food chain. We, too, are part of a food chain. Luckily, like the wise old owl, we are also at the top of our chain. 5

4

1 According to the text, which of the following statements is true?

- ○ Human beings are like owls.
- ○ Human beings do not have natural predators.
- ○ Human beings stay at the top of all food chains.
- ○ Human beings are as wise as owls.

2 What is the setting of this text?

- ○ a forest
- ○ a garden
- ○ a field
- ○ a tree

3 According to the text, which of the following is the order of the food chain?

- ○ lettuce, shrew, beetle, slug, owl
- ○ shrew, lettuce, slug, beetle, owl
- ○ lettuce, slug, beetle, shrew, owl
- ○ slug, lettuce, beetle, shrew, owl

4 In paragraph 3, the author uses the phrase "swoops down" to describe the owl's

- ○ swift action.
- ○ quiet movement.
- ○ cautious movement.
- ○ cunning movement.

5 Which of the following statements is NOT true?

- ○ The owl has no natural predators.
- ○ The shrew preys on the beetle.
- ○ Human beings prey on all animals.
- ○ The lettuce gets energy from the sun.

6 Which would be the best new title for this story?

- ○ The Garden Chain
- ○ The Wise Old Owl
- ○ Understanding the Food Chain
- ○ On Top of the Food Chain

The Four-Star Ranch

Helen woke up to the smell of bacon and eggs. For a moment, she thought she was still in her bed in Vancouver, but then realized that she was in Calgary at the Four-Star Ranch, owned by her Aunt Betty and Uncle Steve. Uncle Steve picked her up at the airport the night before. It had become a yearly tradition for Helen to spend her summer vacation helping out on the ranch. 1

It was half past six and Aunt Betty was making breakfast for the family and wranglers who worked on the ranch. Helen jumped out of bed, pulled on her jeans, T-shirt, boots, and cowboy 2

hat. She quickly said good morning to Aunt Betty on her way out the door. Aunt Betty knew exactly where Helen was going.

3 Helen was at the barn within seconds. She paused in the doorway to take in the smell of fresh hay. Suddenly, a large head popped over the stall door. Dusty, Helen's horse, stood looking at her with his mouth full of hay. He was just as excited to see her as she was to see him. Helen wrapped her arms around the big brown and white horse and gave him a hug. She could hardly wait to put a saddle on Dusty and take him for a long ride around the farm.

4 Helen offered Dusty an apple. As he crunched down on the delicious treat, Helen thought about all the fun things she would do with Dusty. They would herd cattle, go galloping through the fields, swim in the pond, and at the end of the day, she would groom him to make him tidy and shiny. All of a sudden, she heard Aunt Betty sounding the breakfast bell. Helen raced back to the house to eat. Her summer adventure had begun.

5

1 According to the story, Helen had been on the ranch for

- o a day.
- o a night.
- o two nights.
- o the whole summer.

2 Helen went to visit Dusty

- o the night before.
- o before breakfast.
- o after breakfast.
- o in the afternoon.

3 Which of the following would be the best new title for this story?

- o Helen and Dusty
- o Summer Fun at the Four-Star Ranch
- o The Adventure of Helen
- o Aunt Betty and Uncle Steve's Ranch

4 Which word means almost the same as the word "galloping"?

- o running
- o strolling
- o walking
- o racing

5 Read this sentence from paragraph 2.

Aunt Betty knew exactly where Helen was going.

Where was Helen going?

- ○ to the farm
- ○ to the pond
- ○ to the fields
- ○ to the barn

6 Read this sentence from paragraph 4.

As he crunched down on the delicious treat, Helen thought about all the fun things she would do with Dusty.

In this sentence, the word "treat" means

- ○ bacon.
- ○ eggs.
- ○ hay.
- ○ apple.

7 Which of the following sentences shows that Dusty likes Helen?

- ○ Suddenly, a large head popped over the stall door.
- ○ Helen offered Dusty an apple.
- ○ He was just as excited to see her as she was to see him.
- ○ Helen thought about all the fun things she would do with Dusty.

Hat Day at School

1 Sean and Rachel are in grade three at Hillside School. Last week, their class had a special fundraising project. They were raising money for the Red Cross. They have been learning about the important work done by the Red Cross when there is a disaster. It is an organization that provides food and supplies for people in need after a disaster such as a hurricane or flood.

Sean and Rachel were the leaders of the project. Their job was to collect loonies in a big container and then roll them into coin holders for the teacher. 2

Ms. Sharma, their class teacher, had suggested a great way of raising money. Every student would be allowed to wear a hat at school if they paid a loonie to the fundraiser. Usually it is the rule to take off all hats inside the school building. 3

Rachel had another idea – pay an extra loonie and chew gum at school on Hat Day. Ms. Sharma agreed that this was also a great idea. On Hat Day, every student contributed two dollars to the Red Cross. Many students wore hats of special design. 4

It was fun to wear a hat and chew gum at school. Everyone enjoyed Hat Day, including Ms. Sharma. But best of all, it was good to hear the final count from Sean and Rachel – the class had raised $98 for the Red Cross disaster fund. Ms. Sharma congratulated everyone for doing a great job! 5

6

1 According to the story, which of the following statements is true?

- o Ms. Sharma was the leader of the fundraising project.
- o Ms. Sharma was Rachel's teacher.
- o Ms. Sharma was from the Red Cross.
- o Ms. Sharma collected $98.

2 According to the story, which of the following statements is NOT true?

- o Sean and Rachel led a fundraising project.
- o Students each paid $1 to wear a hat on Hat Day.
- o Students each paid $2 to wear a hat and chew gum on Hat Day.
- o Hillside School had collected $98 for the Red Cross.

3 Which of the following statements shows that Ms. Sharma was happy with the fundraising?

- o Everyone enjoyed Hat Day, including Ms. Sharma.
- o Ms. Sharma congratulated everyone for doing a great job!
- o Ms. Sharma, their class teacher, had suggested a great way of raising money.
- o Ms. Sharma agreed that this was also a great idea.

4 Read this sentence from paragraph 4.

Ms. Sharma agreed that this was also a great idea.

What was "a great idea"?

- ○ wearing a hat
- ○ having a Hat Day
- ○ paying one dollar for chewing gum
- ○ paying one dollar for wearing a hat

5 Read this sentence from paragraph 4.

On Hat Day, every student contributed two dollars to the Red Cross.

In this sentence, the word "contributed" means almost the same as

- ○ found.
- ○ donated.
- ○ saved.
- ○ paid.

6 What is the main idea of this story?

- ○ A grade three class raised money for the Red Cross.
- ○ It was a fun Hat Day.
- ○ Rachel suggested having gum on Hat Day.
- ○ Ms. Sharma came up with the idea of a Hat Day.

Recycling Rules

Remember when you throw away,
Use your bins for Recycling Day.

Plastic, glass, styrofoam too,
Put them in the box that's blue.

Cardboard, magazines, papers thrown away, 5
They go in the box that's grey.

Fruit and veggies; meat and lard,
Go in the green bin; it's not hard.

Recycle bins – green, grey, and blue,
They'll save the world for me and you. 10 

Don't overload your garbage can,
Recycle, recycle, whenever you can.

1 According to the poem, which statement is true?

- ○ Food scraps go in the grey box.
- ○ Water bottles should go in the blue box.
- ○ The green bin is for veggies only.
- ○ Garbage is picked up on Garbage Day.

2 Why does the author use an apostrophe for "that's" in line 4?

- ○ to separate the "s" from "that"
- ○ to show how to read the poem
- ○ to make the poem sound better
- ○ to show that a letter has been left out

3 Which of the following words is in short form?

- ○ recycle
- ○ papers
- ○ lard
- ○ veggies

7

4 What do cardboard and magazines have in common?

- ○ They can both be thrown away.
- ○ They are paper products.
- ○ They both go in the blue box.
- ○ They don't overload the garbage can.

5 According to the poem, which statement is NOT true?

- ○ We help save the world by recycling.
- ○ We should know where to put the things for recycling.
- ○ It is easy to remember the recycling rules.
- ○ We should put food scraps in the blue box.

6 Read the line below.

Don't overload your garbage can,

Which of the following lines goes best with it?

- ○ Recycling is the best way to go.
- ○ Follow closely the recycling plan.
- ○ Let's join hands to save the world.
- ○ You must remember to recycle.

7 Do you think "Recycling Rules" is a good title for this poem? Explain why you think so. Use information from the text and your own ideas in your answer.

8 After reading the poem, what are your feelings about recycling? Use information from the text and your own ideas in your answer.

Larry's Outing to a Castle

1 Larry sat at the back of the yellow school bus. He was very excited. It was a long and bumpy ride but it was all worth it. Today, Larry and his classmates were visiting a real castle.

2 The bus finally came to a stop in front of a magnificent building. Larry could not believe his eyes. The castle was just like the ones that he

had seen in books and movies. The children walked excitedly across a drawbridge and reached the entrance to the castle.

3 Mr. Greene greeted the students at the entrance. He was going to take them on a tour through the castle. He explained to the children that they would be seeing many old and interesting artifacts. He also reminded them not to wander off alone because it was very easy to get lost in this old, enormous castle and there were some parts of the castle that were off limits to visitors.

4 Larry was not listening; he was far too busy staring at something standing at the end of a long corridor. Then he slowly moved closer to examine the object. It was a large, silver suit of armour. Beside the armour was a closed door with a sign. On the sign were the words, "DO NOT ENTER". Larry could not resist the temptation. He felt his hand moving toward the doorknob...

8

1 Which of the following shows that Larry was looking eagerly forward to the trip to the castle?

- ○ it was all worth it
- ○ a long and bumpy ride
- ○ a magnificent building
- ○ many old and interesting artifacts

2 Why does the story end with "..."?

- ○ to show that Larry was nervous
- ○ to let readers think what would happen next
- ○ to show that the door could not be opened
- ○ to show that Larry did not know what to do next

3 Read this sentence from paragraph 4.

Larry could not resist the temptation.

What was the temptation?

- ○ to examine the armour
- ○ to put on the armour
- ○ to take off the "DO NOT ENTER" sign
- ○ to open the door

4 Which would be the best new title for this story?

- ○ Mischievous Larry
- ○ Larry's Adventure in the Castle
- ○ A Memorable Outing
- ○ An Exciting Trip

5 Explain what kind of person you think Larry is and tell why you think so. Use information from the story and your own ideas in your answer.

6 What do you think might happen when Larry turned the doorknob?

Trees

Have you ever noticed the many kinds of trees we see every day? Some trees have broad leaves that turn brown and drop off in the fall. These are called deciduous trees. Other trees have narrow leaves that stay green on the trees all year round. We call these coniferous trees. 1

All trees have trunks to support them and bark to protect the trunk from insects and diseases. What is interesting about tree trunks is that the trunk can tell the age of the tree. When the trunk is cut, it shows rings and by counting the rings, 2 we can tell how many years the tree has been alive. One ring represents one year.

3 People use trees for food, housing, furniture, paper, and a variety of wooden objects. Fruit trees such as apple, peach, and pear give us food to eat. Softwood trees grow quickly, so they provide most of the wood used for building houses. Softwood comes from coniferous trees such as pine and spruce. The wood from hardwood trees is more expensive because it may take up to a hundred years before they grow big enough to be used. Some well-known hardwood trees are walnut, oak, maple, and beech. These woods are often used for making furniture.

4 Trees have grown in nature for thousands of years. They are important to the environment because they give off oxygen that all human beings and animals need for breathing. Trees also provide homes for wildlife. Every year, tens of thousands of trees are being cut down for people to use. It is important to replace these trees by growing new ones so that trees will always be available in the future.

9

1 Using information from the text, list four things that are different between deciduous trees and coniferous trees.

TREES

Deciduous	Coniferous

2 Give two examples to show how trees are also important to animals. Use information from the text.

3 Explain why it is important to plant new trees. Use information from the text and your own ideas in your answer.

4 What would happen if people used hardwood for building houses?

Country Sights

A drive in the country,

What an awesome scene!

Miles and miles of cornfields,

Growing tall and green.

Farmers driving tractors, 5

Under the red hot sun.

Roadside stands with veggies,

Food for everyone!

Tall silos in the distance,
Barns and stables too. 10
Fields piled with haystacks,
Under a sky of blue.

Cows gently grazing,
Horses running free.
Driving in the country, 15
It's where I love to be!

1 According to the poem, which statement is true?

- ○ Farmers drive their tractors through the cornfields.
- ○ There are many cornfields.
- ○ The writer drives through the cornfields.
- ○ Corn is growing next to vegetables.

2 Why does the author use an exclamation mark at the end of line 2?

- ○ to show that the driving is exciting
- ○ to show his excitement about the trip
- ○ to show the spectacular view he sees
- ○ to show that he does not believe in what he sees

10

3 According to the poem, in which season does the author make the trip?

- ○ spring
- ○ summer
- ○ fall
- ○ winter

4 Choose one stanza (section) of the poem. Write it out in complete sentences.

____

____

____

____

____

5 Use information from the poem to show that the weather is good when the author visits the countryside.

____

____

____

____

____

6 Do you think "Country Sights" is a good title for this poem? Use information from the poem and your own ideas in your answer.

7 After reading the poem, what are your feelings about the countryside? Use information from the poem and your own ideas in your answer.

1 On your way to school, you saw a stray dog on the street. Write a short story. Describe the dog and tell what happened.

Ideas for My Story

REMEMBER: ***check your spelling, grammar, and punctuation.***

Now write a story, **The Stray Dog**.

1

2 Read the sentence. Part of the sentence is missing.

When the doorbell ______, we were having dinner.

Which of the following correctly completes the sentence?

- ○ ringing
- ○ rings
- ○ rang
- ○ was ringing

3 Which of the following words begins with a prefix?

- ○ immense
- ○ important
- ○ imitate
- ○ impolite

4 Which word below goes with "tree" to make a compound word?

- ○ top
- ○ branch
- ○ trunk
- ○ bark

5 Read the sentences below.

The children were at Martha's birthday party. They had birthday cake and yummy food. They played fun games, too.

Which of the following is the best way to combine these sentences?

- ○ At Martha's birthday party, they had birthday cake and yummy food and they played fun games, too.
- ○ The children were at Martha's birthday party, and they had birthday cake and yummy food, and they played fun games, too.
- ○ At Martha's birthday party, the children had birthday cake and yummy food, and they played fun games, too.
- ○ The children at Martha's birthday party had birthday cake, yummy food, and fun games.

6 Which of the following words is NOT correct?

- ○ putting
- ○ sobing
- ○ dyeing
- ○ skiing

1 Your class is planning an outing and your teacher is asking for suggestions of where to go. Write the place you think is best for the outing. Explain why you feel this is the best place to go.

Ideas for My Writing

Remember: ***check your spelling, grammar, and punctuation.***

Write your suggestion here.

2

2 Which of the following words begins with a prefix?

- ○ unit
- ○ under
- ○ undo
- ○ unite

3 Choose the word in the sentence that describes the man.

The old man pointed to a box near him.

- ○ pointed
- ○ old
- ○ near
- ○ him

4 Read the sentence below.

They enjoy _______ baseball after school.

Which of the following words correctly completes the sentence?

- ○ play
- ○ plays
- ○ playing
- ○ played

5 Read the sentence below.

Mrs. Baker let the children share the candies ______ themselves.

Which of the following words correctly completes the sentence?

- ○ with
- ○ among
- ○ for
- ○ between

6 Read the sentences below.

Ming can't find his journal. Ming looks everywhere. His sister looks everywhere for him too.

Which of the following is the best way to combine these sentences?

- ○ Ming and his sister look everywhere but they can't find Ming's journal.
- ○ Ming can't find his journal and he looks everywhere and his sister looks eveywhere for him too.
- ○ Ming's sister and Ming look everywhere for his journal but Ming's sister and Ming can't find his journal.
- ○ Ming looks everywhere and his sister looks everywhere and they can't find his journal.

1 Your parents will give you a pet for your birthday.

Write about the pet that you would like to have. Explain why you want this pet and how you would take care of it.

Ideas for My Writing

Remember: ***check your spelling, grammar, and punctuation.***

3

2 Read the sentence below.

We will ______ at the hotel for two nights.

Which of the following correctly completes the sentence?

- ○ stay
- ○ to stay
- ○ staying
- ○ be stay

3 Read the sentence below.

We have not ______ each other for a long time.

Which of the following words correctly completes the sentence?

- ○ see
- ○ saw
- ○ seeing
- ○ seen

4 Which of the following words is NOT a compound word?

- ○ beginner
- ○ housekeeper
- ○ salesman
- ○ woodpecker

5 Choose the word in the sentence that describes the children.

The drama teacher thinks that the children are too timid.

- ○ thinks
- ○ timid
- ○ drama
- ○ too

6 Read the sentences below.

We went on a field trip yesterday. It was fun. We enjoyed ourselves very much.

Which of the following is the best way to combine these sentences?

- ○ We went on a field trip yesterday and it was fun and we enjoyed ourselves very much.
- ○ We went on a field trip yesterday so we enjoyed ourselves very much and it was fun.
- ○ We enjoyed ourselves very much on a field trip yesterday and it was fun.
- ○ Yesterday's field trip was fun and we enjoyed ourselves very much.

1 Write a short story. In your story, there should be a little boy, an ice cream, and a squirrel.

Ideas for My Story

REMEMBER: ***check your spelling, grammar, and punctuation.***

2 Read the sentence below. Part of the sentence is missing.

Jay always ______ the books on time.

Which of the following correctly completes the sentence?

- o return
- o returns
- o returning
- o is returning

3 Read the sentence below. Part of the sentence is missing.

She came home ______ and her mother was worried.

Which of the following words correctly completes the sentence?

- o late
- o lately
- o later
- o latest

4 Which word below goes with "cake" to make a compound word?

- o birthday
- o cup
- o chocolate
- o wedding

5 Choose the word in the sentence that describes how the children were singing.

The little children were singing sweetly in the school concert.

- ○ sweetly
- ○ little
- ○ concert
- ○ school

6 Read the sentences below.

We can have a game of baseball after school. We can watch a video after school. We can only choose one to do after school.

Which of the following is the best way to combine these sentences?

- ○ We can have a game of baseball after school and we can watch a video after school and we can only choose one to do.
- ○ We can either have a game of baseball or watch a video after school.
- ○ We can have a game of baseball after school or we can watch a video and we can only choose one to do.
- ○ We can have a game of baseball or we can watch a video after school but we can only choose one to do after school.

LANGUAGE

Assessment of Reading and Writing

Grade

3

Grandma's Quilt

My grandmother lives on a farm and I love
to visit her there. She has lots of antique
furniture and many interesting old items.
One of my favourite things is an old quilt
that was made over fifty years ago. 5
Grandma had it when she was a little girl
and she calls it her "story quilt". Her mother
made it with different patches of material.
Each square of cloth came from old clothing
or household items and Grandma has a 10
story to tell about each piece. The quilt is
like a record of the family past.

There is a green velvet square from Grandma's favourite skirt and some corduroy fabric from her brother's overalls. 15
There is a square of white satin from a wedding dress and a piece of embroidered linen from an old pillow case. There are quite a few squares of flowered material from the colourful dresses the little girls 20
used to wear. In the centre of the quilt, there is a beautiful rose design. Grandma told me that it was once a tapestry cushion from the front parlour. One day, the cat tore the cushion so her mother saved the 25
rose for her quilt.

I think that this quilt, which was made from old scraps of material, is worth more than all the brand new bedding we buy today. It is warm and cozy and pretty but best of all, 30
it has a story to tell.

1 Which word means almost the same as "antique"?

- o beautiful
- o old
- o expensive
- o comfortable

2 According to the text, which of the following statements is true?

- o Some corduroy fabric was from a wedding dress.
- o The rose design was from Grandma's pillow.
- o A green velvet square was from a cushion.
- o There was a patch of linen from a pillow case.

3 Read this sentence from the text (lines 6–7).

Grandma had it when she was a little girl and she calls it her "story quilt".

The quotation marks are used to show that

- o the quilt can tell stories.
- o "story quilt" is a special name given to the quilt by Grandma.
- o the quilt is like a storybook.
- o the quilt is as interesting as a story.

4 Which of the following statements is NOT true?

- ○ Grandma's mother made the quilt for Grandma.
- ○ Grandma made the quilt when she was very young.
- ○ The author likes the story quilt very much.
- ○ The story quilt was made from old scraps of material.

5 Read this sentence from the text (lines 9–11).

Each square of cloth came from old clothing or household items and Grandma has a story to tell about each piece.

Which of the following are household items?

- ○ overalls
- ○ wedding dresses
- ○ cushions
- ○ skirts

6 What kind of text is this piece of reading?

- ○ a report
- ○ a journal entry
- ○ a story
- ○ a letter

7 Which would be the best new title for this text?

- ○ Grandma's Story Quilt
- ○ The Old Story Quilt
- ○ A Record of the Family Past
- ○ A Quilt You Can't Buy

8 Read this sentence from the text (lines 27–29).

I think that this quilt, which was made from old scraps of material, is worth more than all the brand new bedding we buy today.

Explain why the author thinks this way. Use information from the text and your own ideas in your answer.

9 Write a paragraph about a toy that you like best. Describe how it looks. Tell how you got it and why you love it so much.

Ideas for My Paragraph

REMEMBER: ***check your spelling, grammar, and punctuation.***

10 Read this sentence.

I have never seen such a colourful quilt before.

Which of the following words describes "quilt"?

- ○ never
- ○ seen
- ○ such
- ○ colourful

11 Which of the following words has a prefix?

- ○ divide
- ○ discover
- ○ dish
- ○ distance

12 Which of the following is a compound word?

- ○ handyman
- ○ mango
- ○ many
- ○ mantis

13 Which of the following belongs in this sentence?

They ______ a group dance before the concert.

- o performs
- o performing
- o will perform
- o are perform

14 Which of the following best completes this sentence?

I saw ______ stranger waiting outside the office.

- o a
- o an
- o this
- o that

15 Which of the following best completes this sentence?

Janet did not know ______.

- o he
- o him
- o his
- o himself

Water Safety

Playing in water is fun but it can be dangerous if you do not pay attention to safety.

The first rule of water safety is to be always with a buddy. If you have a problem, your friend can come to your rescue or go and get help. 5

Also, it is best to have an adult present, especially if you are not good at swimming. You should never swim at a beach where there is no lifeguard or adult. 10

Swimming pools are usually well supervised but you can still get injured if you are not careful. Most injuries are a result of running carelessly and slipping on wet surfaces. You should avoid chasing and running on the pool side. If you are a beginning swimmer, you should stay in the shallow end of the pool. 15

If you want to swim in a river or a lake, find out what is below the water surface before plunging in. Often there are submerged rocks or branches that you can't see. If you jump or dive into unknown waters, you may seriously injure yourself on a hidden object. 20

If you are at a cottage, you may have the chance to go boating. When you are in a boat, you should always wear a life jacket. 25

16 Read this sentence from the text (lines 16–18).

If you are a beginning swimmer, you should stay in the shallow end of the pool.

Which of the following means the opposite of "shallow"?

- ○ dangerous
- ○ deep
- ○ wide
- ○ narrow

17 Read this sentence from the text (lines 21–22).

Often there are submerged rocks or branches that you can't see.

Which of the following means almost the same as "submerged"?

- ○ underwater
- ○ big
- ○ sharp
- ○ dangerous

18 According to the text, which of the following statements is true?

- ○ We should not swim in rivers or lakes.
- ○ There may be hidden objects in rivers or lakes.
- ○ We should only swim in swimming pools.
- ○ We should wear life jackets when we swim.

19 On your way home from school, you saw a backpack hanging from a tree.

Write a paragraph about what you would do.

Ideas for My Paragraph

Remember: ***check your spelling, grammar, and punctuation.***

20 Read this sentence.

Yesterday he ______ home for school at about seven o'clock.

Which of the following best completes the sentence?

- ○ left
- ○ leave
- ○ leaves
- ○ leaving

21 Read this sentence.

The birthday party began at four in the afternoon and the children played ______ seven in the evening.

Which of the following best completes the sentence?

- ○ for
- ○ to
- ○ at
- ○ until

22 Which of the following words is wrong in spelling?

- ○ biting
- ○ beatting
- ○ beaten
- ○ bitten

23 Read this sentence.

The tired players were enjoying ice cream cones after the exciting ball game.

Which of the following words describes "ball game"?

- o tired
- o enjoying
- o ice
- o exciting

24 Read the sentences below.

Summer is hot and sunny. The boys enjoy swimming in the pool. The pool is in John's backyard.

Which of the following is the best way to combine these sentences?

- o In the hot and sunny summer, the boys enjoy swimming in the pool in John's backyard.
- o Summer is hot and sunny, and the boys enjoy swimming in the pool; the pool is in John's backyard.
- o In the hot and sunny summer, the boys enjoy swimming in the pool and the pool is in John's backyard.
- o Summer is hot and sunny, and the boys enjoy swimming in the pool in John's backyard.

Reading Practice 1

1. an article
2. things that are special about the sunflower
3. famous
4. Sunflowers can turn to face the sun.
5. attractive
6. cloth
7. Black oil sunflower seeds are good for making salad.

Reading Practice 2

1. to show that she was surprised
2. boots and skis.
3. an inverted V shape.
4. I was pretty nervous about how I would make it down the hill.
5. exciting
6. Jean-Luc, Angela's parents, and Angela

Reading Practice 3

1. It was no exception this year.
2. satisfied with what they had done
3. outdoors.
4. tasted.
5. Mrs. Romano
6. The Romanos' "Tomato Sauce" Day

Reading Practice 4

1. Human beings do not have natural predators.
2. a garden
3. lettuce, slug, beetle, shrew, owl
4. swift action.
5. Human beings prey on all animals.
6. The Garden Chain

Reading Practice 5

1. a night.
2. before breakfast.
3. Summer Fun at the Four-Star Ranch
4. running
5. to the barn
6. apple.
7. He was just as excited to see her as she was to see him.

Reading Practice 6

1. Ms. Sharma was Rachel's teacher.
2. Hillside School had collected $98 for the Red Cross.
3. Everyone enjoyed Hat Day, including Ms. Sharma.
4. paying one dollar for chewing gum
5. donated.
6. A grade three class raised money for the Red Cross.

Reading Practice 7

1. Water bottles should go in the blue box.
2. to show that a letter has been left out
3. veggies
4. They are paper products.
5. We should put food scraps in the blue box.
6. Follow closely the recycling plan.

7-8. (Individual answers)

Reading Practice 8

1. it was all worth it
2. to let readers think what would happen next
3. to open the door
4. Larry's Adventure in the Castle

5-6. (Individual answers)

Reading Practice 9

1. TREES

Deciduous	Coniferous
• broad leaves	• narrow leaves
• leaves turn brown and drop off in the fall	• leaves stay green on the tree all year round
• hardwood	• softwood
• used for making furniture	• used for building houses

2. Trees give off oxygen that animals need for breathing.
   Trees provide homes for wildlife.

3-4. (Individual answers)

Reading Practice 10

1. There are many cornfields.
2. to show the spectacular view he sees
3. summer

4-7. (Individual answers)

Writing Practice 1

1. (Individual writing)
2. rang
3. impolite
4. treetop
5. The children at Martha's birthday party had birthday cake, yummy food, and fun games.
6. sobing

Writing Practice 2

1. (Individual writing)
2. undo
3. old
4. playing
5. among
6. Ming and his sister look everywhere but they can't find Ming's journal.

Writing Practice 3

1. (Individual writing)
2. stay
3. seen
4. beginner
5. timid
6. Yesterday's field trip was fun and we enjoyed ourselves very much.

Writing Practice 4

1. (Individual writing)
2. returns
3. late
4. cupcake
5. sweetly
6. We can either have a game of baseball or watch a video after school.

Assessment of Reading and Writing

1. old
2. There was a patch of linen from a pillow case.
3. "story quilt" is a special name given to the quilt by Grandma.
4. Grandma made the quilt when she was very young.
5. cushions
6. a story
7. Grandma's Story Quilt
8. (Individual answer)
9. (Individual writing)
10. colourful
11. discover
12. handyman
13. will perform
14. a
15. him
16. deep
17. underwater
18. There may be hidden objects in rivers or lakes.
19. (Individual writing)
20. left
21. until
22. beatting
23. exciting
24. In the hot and sunny summer, the boys enjoy swimming in the pool in John's backyard.

Contents

Printed in China

Test-taking TIPS

General

- Count the number of pages to make sure that there are no missing pages.
- Read the instructions carefully so that you know what to do and how to do it.
- Write neatly.
- Always check your answers and writing after you have completed the test.
- Skip the questions that you are stuck on and come back to them after completing the rest of the test.

MULTIPLE CHOICE

- Read through the test quickly. Skip the difficult questions and do the easy ones first.
- Read the question twice before finding the answer.
- Look for keywords in the question. (e.g. "fewer" suggests a subtraction problem; "share...equally" suggests a division problem)
- Come up with the answer in your head before looking at the possible answers.
- Read all the four options before deciding which is the correct answer.
- Eliminate the options that you know are incorrect.

PROBLEM SOLVING

- Read the whole question carefully and never make any assumptions about what the question might be.
- Highlight (i.e. underline / circle) the important information in the question.
- Translate the words into mathematical terms.
- Use drawings to help you better understand the question.
- Break down the problem into several parts and solve them one by one.
- Know exactly what needs to be included in your solution.
- Estimate the answer.
- Before writing out the solution, organize your thoughts.
- For a question that involves measurements,

  – make sure the measurements are uniform when solving the problem.
  – the measurement in the answer is converted to the unit that is asked.
- Use words to describe what you are calculating.
- Always write a concluding sentence for your solution.
- Check if your answer is reasonable (i.e. Is the answer close to your estimate?).
- Never leave a question blank. Show your work or write down your thoughts. Even if you do not get the correct answer, you might get some marks for your work.

1 Look at the money that Sue has.

How many quarters can Sue trade at the most?

- O 14
- O 10
- O 15
- O 12

2 Which point shows 615 on the number line?

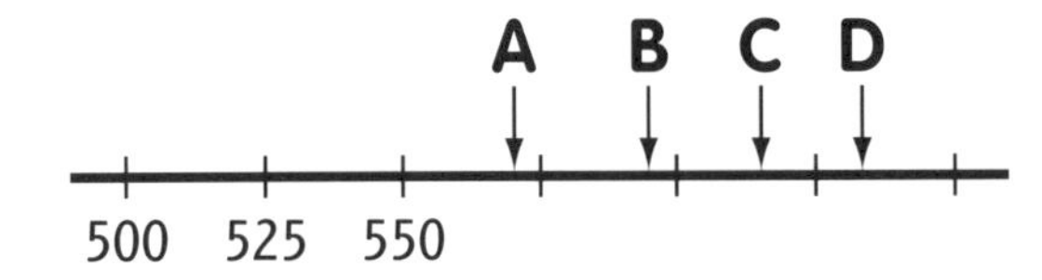

- O A
- O B
- O C
- O D

3 Look at the ribbon below.

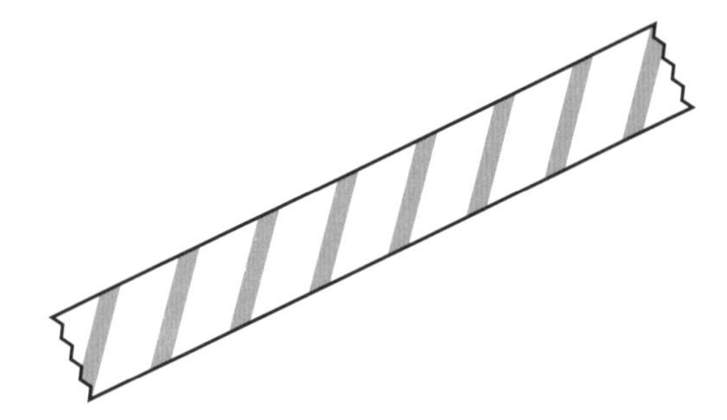

Measure to find the length of the ribbon.

- O a bit longer than 6 cm
- O a bit shorter than 7 cm
- O exactly 7 cm
- O a bit longer than 7 cm

4 Which figure can be formed using the net below?

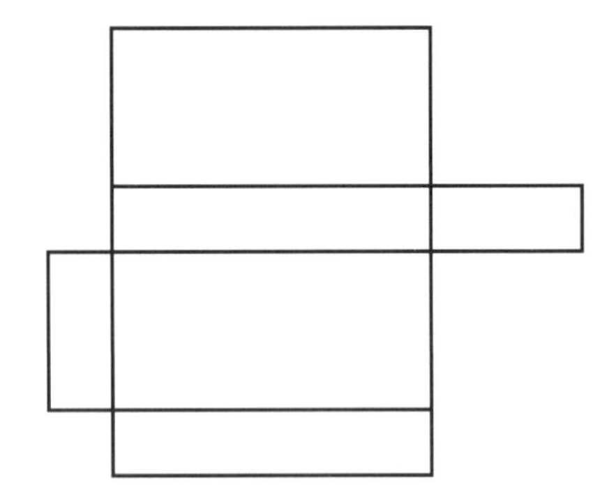

- O triangular pyramid
- O rectangular prism
- O square-based prism
- O cube

5 The clock below shows the the time when Michael finished his breakfast.

What time did Michael start his breakfast?

- o 8:00
- o 7:15
- o 6:20
- o 7:45

6 Kevin uses estimation to solve the following problem.

$$\begin{array}{r} 341 \\ -\ 289 \\ \hline \end{array}$$

Which is closest to the difference?

- o 340 – 280
- o 350 – 290
- o 350 – 280
- o 340 – 290

7 Look at the pattern.

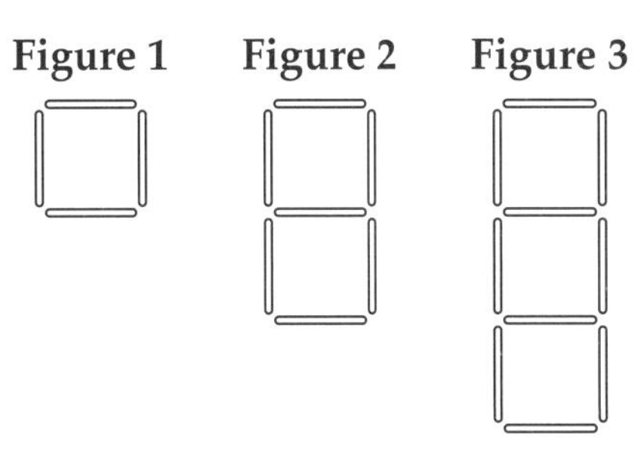

Follow the pattern to find the number of sticks in Figure 5.

- o 16
- o 13
- o 15
- o 14

8 Leo has a bag of 15 marbles. The marbles are either red or yellow. The number of red marbles doubles the number of yellow marbles. Leo draws a marble from the bag without looking. Which best describes the chance that Leo gets a yellow marble?

- o certain
- o likely
- o unlikely
- o impossible

9 Linda and Andy use pictographs to record their stickers. Look at their pictographs.

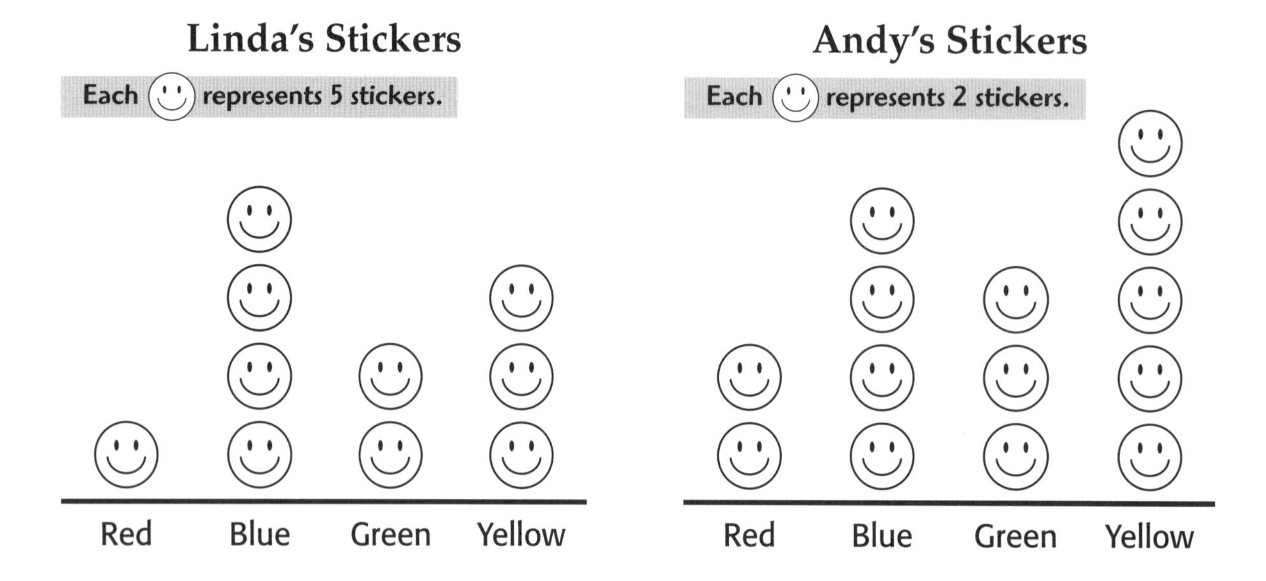

Andy thinks that he has more stickers than Linda. Is he right?

Explain Your Thinking

10 This list shows the number of apples that each customer buys.

8	16	5	3	7	10	21	17
3	15	18	18	2	24	15	13
14	11	7	19	2	14	13	12

Organize the data in the tally chart. What is the range of the number of apples that most customers buy?

Show Your Work

Number of Apples	Number of Customers
1 – 5	
6 – 10	
11 – 15	
16 – 20	
21 – 25	

1 Mr. Smith always takes a walk of 20 minutes after dinner. If Mr. Smith finished his walk at 7:10 p.m. tonight, what time did he start his walk?

- ○ 6:30 p.m.
- ○ 6:50 p.m.
- ○ 7:30 p.m.
- ○ 6:50 a.m.

2 Jason is finding the answer to this subtraction sentence.

58 – 27 = ☐

Which number sentence should he use to check the answer?

- ○ 58 + 27 = 85
- ○ 31 + 27 = 58
- ○ 58 – 25 = 33
- ○ 31 + 27 + 27 = 58 + 27

3 There are 463 red balls and 209 blue balls in a box. If Judy takes out 243 balls from the box, how many balls will be left?

- ○ 11
- ○ 429
- ○ 497
- ○ 915

4 Erin wants to build a pyramid using all of the following sticks and modelling clay.

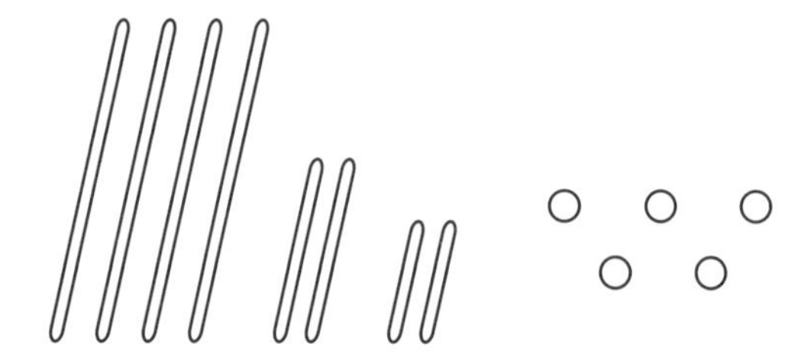

Which pyramid can she build?

- ○ triangular pyramid
- ○ rectangular pyramid
- ○ pentagonal pyramid
- ○ hexagonal pyramid

5 The graph shows the results of a survey of the children's favourite food for lunch.

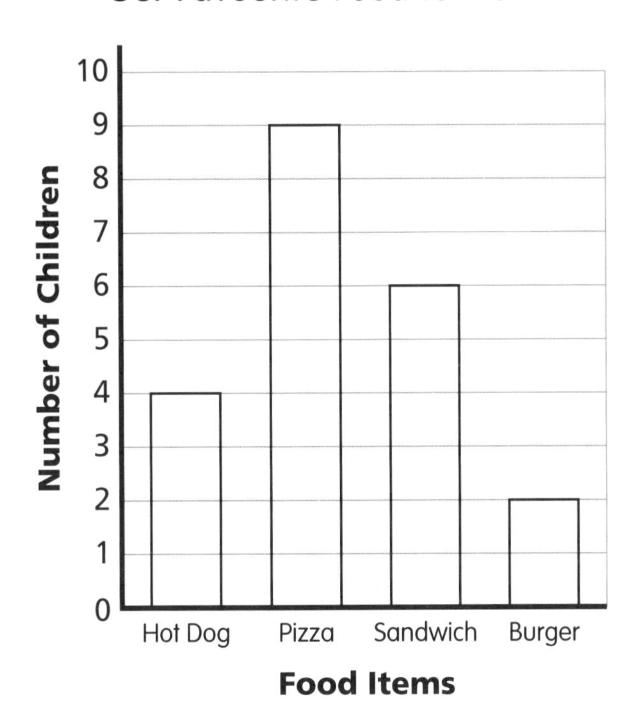

How many more children like pizzas than burgers?

- O 2
- O 3
- O 4
- O 7

6 How many line(s) of symmetry does the shape have?

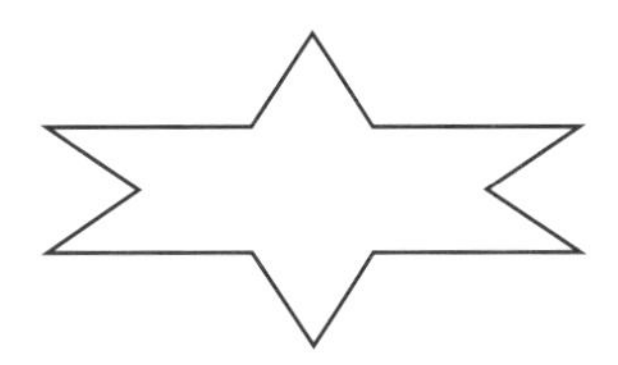

- O 0
- O 1
- O 2
- O 3

7 Look at the pattern.

85, 89, 86, 90, 87, 91, ...

What are the next two numbers?

- O 95, 92
- O 88, 85
- O 95, 99
- O 88, 92

8 Which number is greater than 388 but smaller than 436?

- O 368
- O 398
- O 440
- O 446

2

9 There are 17 children in Mrs. Smith's senior kindergarten class. Mrs. Smith needs helpers for a class outing. Each helper takes care of 5 children.

How many helpers does Mrs. Smith need?

Use a diagram to illustrate your answer.

Explain Your Thinking

10 Andrew sorted the figures into two groups. His sorting rule is "rectangular faces" and "6 vertices".

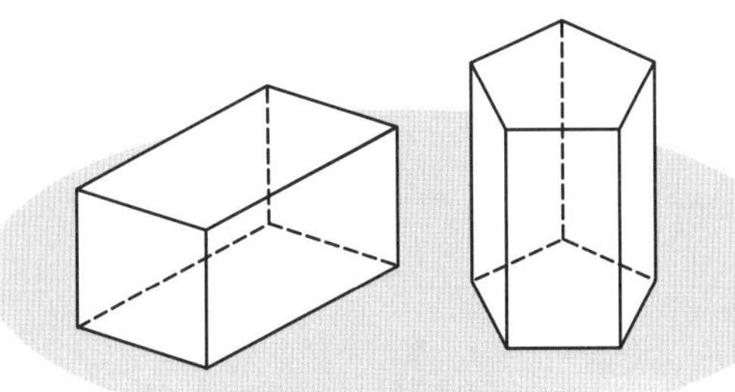

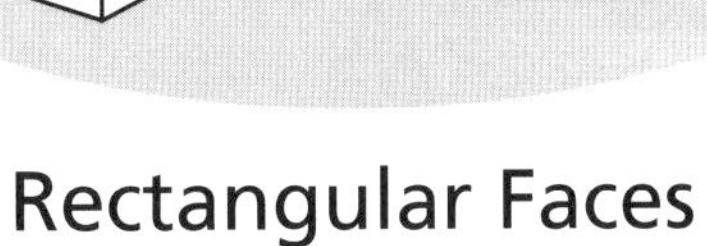

Rectangular Faces

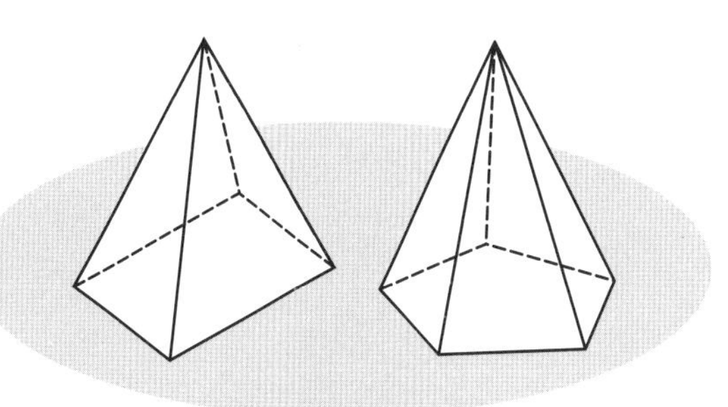

6 Vertices

Andrew's friend, Kelly, found that he misplaced one figure. Name the misplaced figure and explain.

Explain Your Thinking

1 Sarah filled 4 glasses with 1 litre of juice. How many glasses does she need to hold 6 litres of juice?

- ○ 4
- ○ 5
- ○ 24
- ○ 30

2 These are Judy's stickers.

If Judy gives one fourth of her stickers to Katie, how many stickers will she have left?

- ○ 3
- ○ 6
- ○ 8
- ○ 9

3 Which dotted line is the line of symmetry of the triangle?

○ 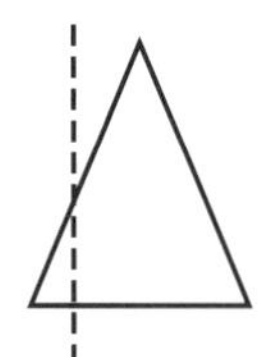

○ 

○ 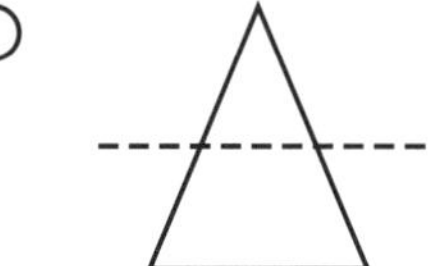

○ 

4 What is the answer in expanded form to the addition below?

276 + 149 = ?

- ○ 500 + 20 + 4
- ○ 40 + 200 + 5
- ○ 400 + 50 + 2
- ○ 400 + 20 + 5

5 Look at the pattern.

Figure 1	Figure 2	Figure 3
● □ ●	● □ ● ● □ ●	● □ ● ● □ ● ● □ ●

How many circles and squares are needed for the next figure?

- o 4 ○ and 8 ■
- o 8 ○ and 4 ■
- o 8 ● and 8 □
- o 8 ● and 4 □

6 Estimate the answer to the vertical subtraction below.

$$\begin{array}{r} 81 \\ -\ 48 \\ \hline \end{array}$$

- o about 30
- o about 40
- o about 50
- o about 130

7 Jane has 16 scarves. 4 of them are blue and 2 of them are red. She picks a scarf randomly without looking. What is the chance that the scarf she picks is not blue or red?

- o certain
- o likely
- o unlikely
- o impossible

8 Measure the sides of the shape below.

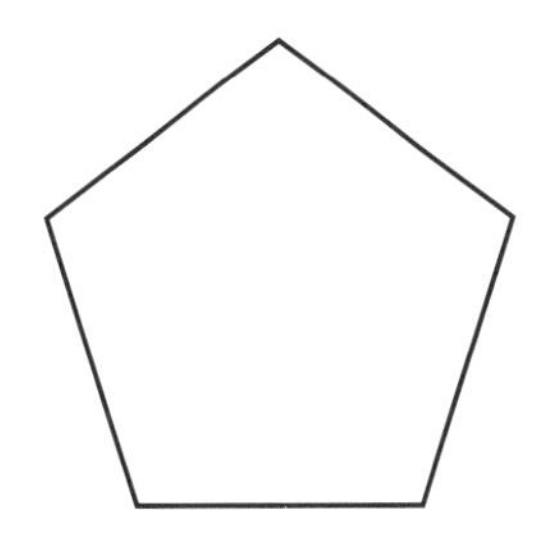

What is its perimeter in centimetres?

- o 5
- o 6
- o 10
- o 12

9 ABC Department Store is going to hold a lucky draw. The saleswoman, Mrs. Dickson, has proposed two ways to put different balls in the box. The ways are as follows:

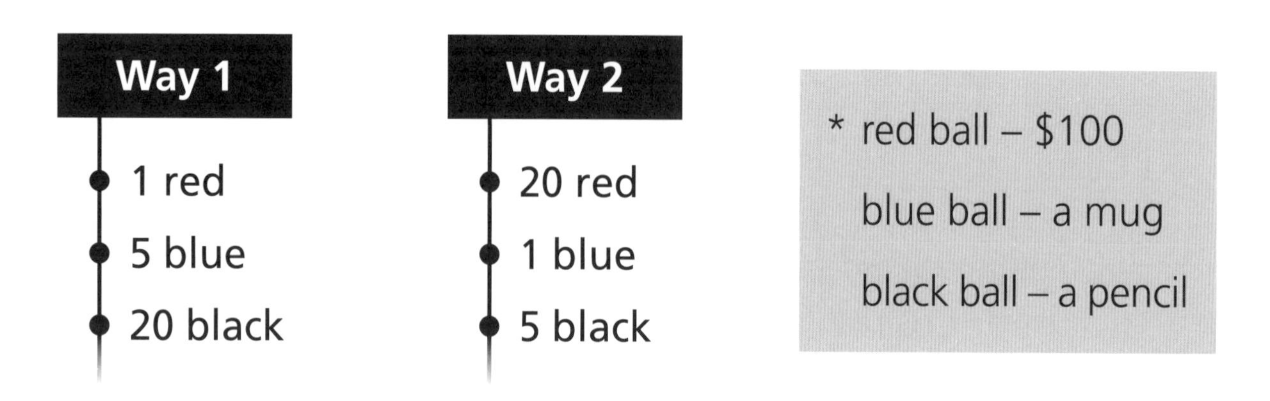

If you were the manager of the store, which way would you use? Give reasons.

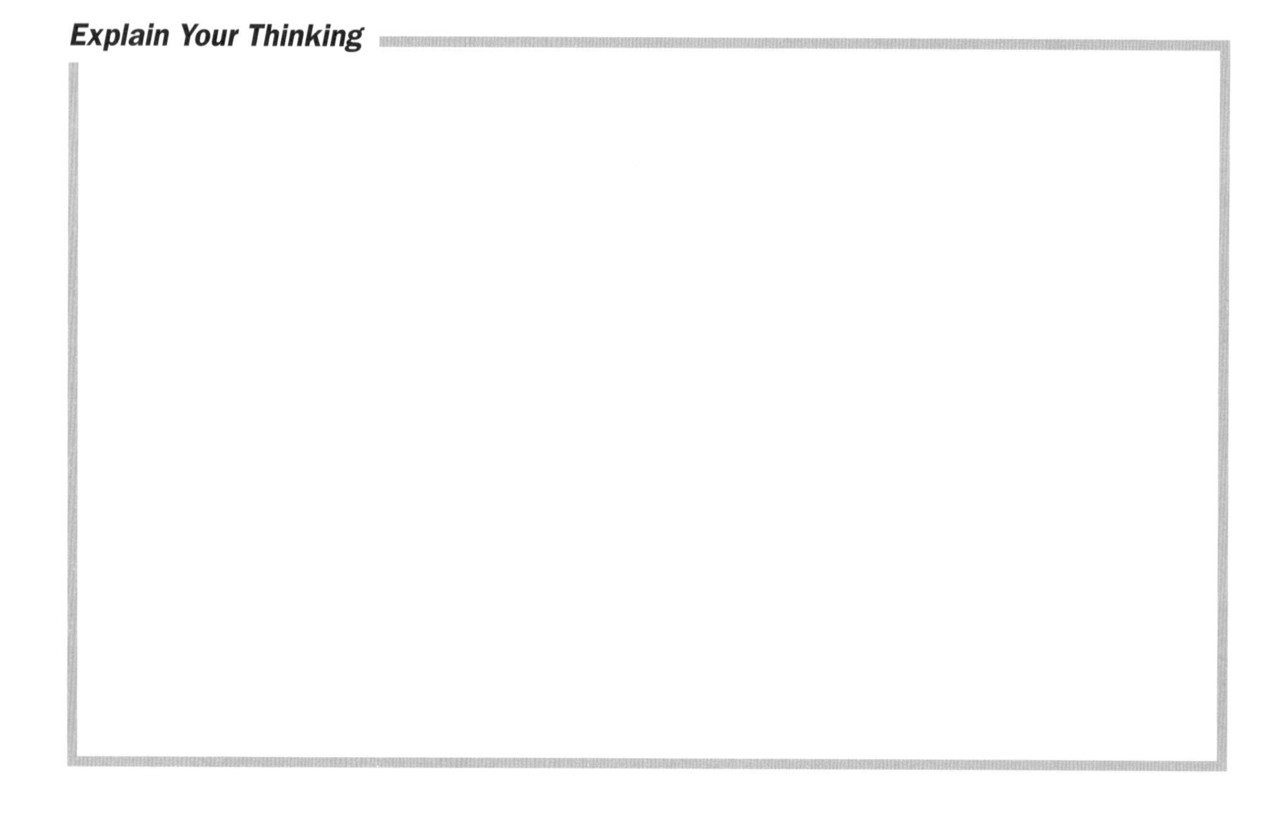

10 Mr. White buys a newspaper on Saturday. Look at the coins that Mr. White has.

Sunny News	
Mon – Fri	$0.75 each
Sat	$1.25 each
Sun	$1.50 each

If Mr. White uses the fewest coins to pay for a newspaper, which coins will he have left? What is the total value?

Explain Your Thinking

1 The dotted line is the line of symmetry of the L-shape.

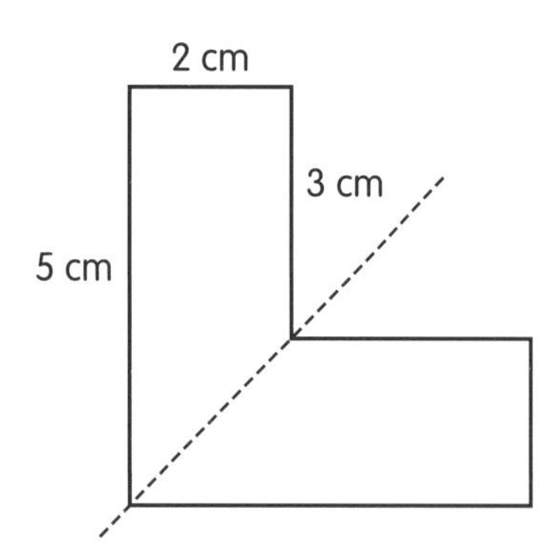

What is the perimeter of the L-shape?

- O 10 cm
- O 16 cm
- O 20 cm
- O 24 cm

2 Look at the pattern.

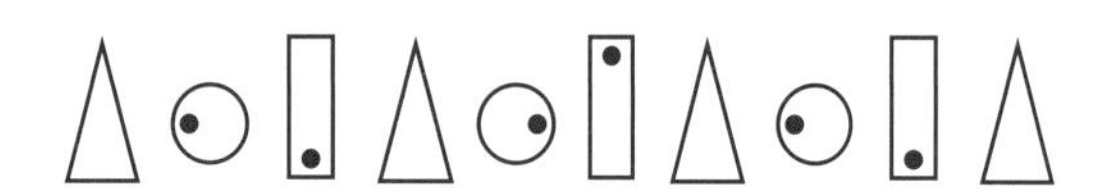

Following the pattern, what are the next two shapes?

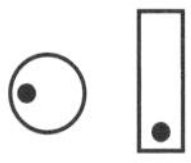

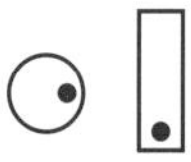

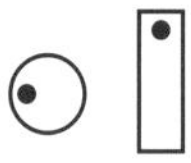

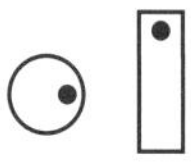

3 The clock shows the time that Judy starts practising the piano.

If Judy practises the piano for 35 minutes, at what time will she finish?

- O 4:10
- O 5:05
- O 5:20
- O 5:45

4 Jill pays a toonie for a hot dog which costs $1.75. What is her change?

- O a penny
- O a nickel
- O a dime
- O a quarter

5 Which number is greater than 620 but smaller than 637?

- 639
- 617
- 629
- 699

6 Helen wants to make a pentagonal pyramid with straws and modelling clay.

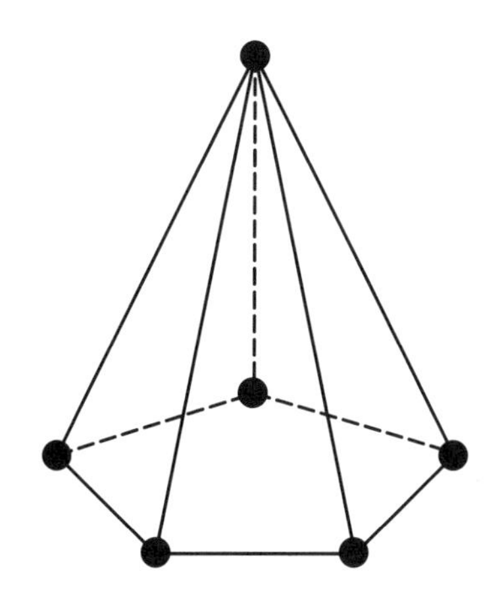

How many straws does she need?

- 6
- 10
- 12
- 15

7 The pictograph shows the number of stickers that the children have.

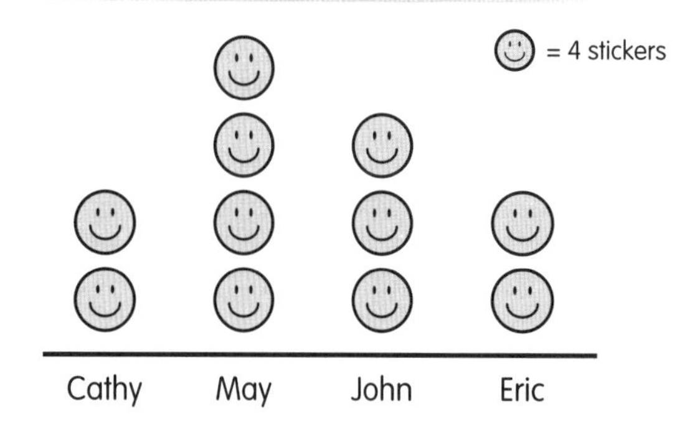

How many stickers do the girls have in all?

- 6
- 20
- 24
- 44

8 Tim has 127 red paper clips and 52 green ones. If Eva has 34 more paper clips than Tim, how many paper clips does Eva have?

- 145
- 109
- 41
- 213

9 Katie bought 16 lollipops on Wednesday. The number of lollipops that Katie bought on Thursday was 4 more than that on Wednesday.

Katie puts all the lollipops that she bought in these two days equally into 4 bags. How many lollipops are there in each bag?

Explain Your Thinking

10 Look at the shapes that Jason drew.

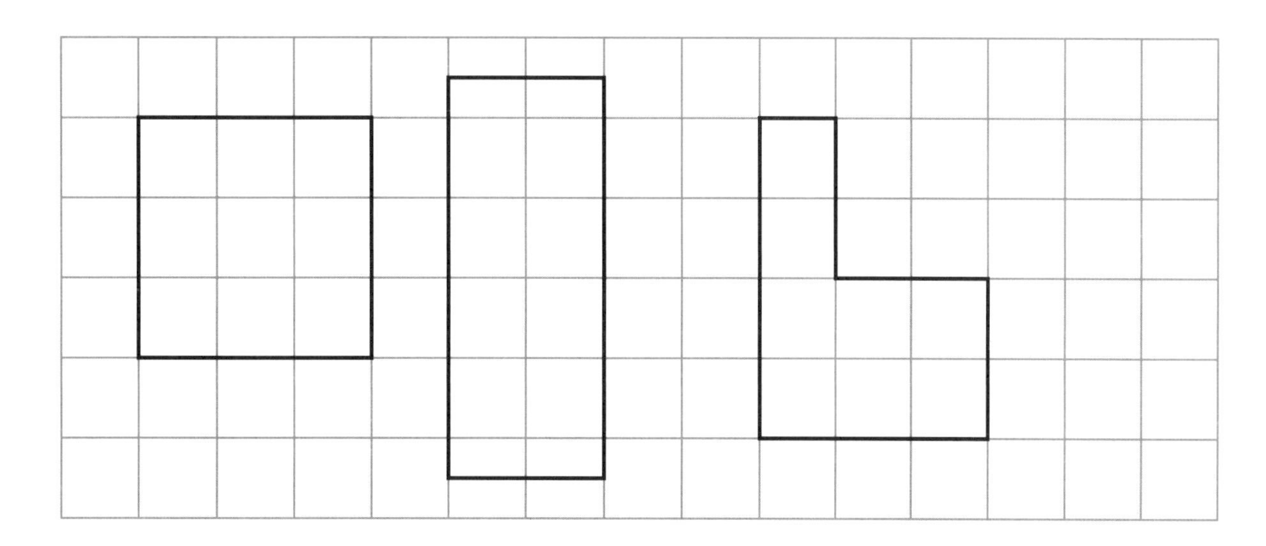

Jason says, "The square has the least perimeter, so it has the least area." Is he correct? If not, what is the correct answer?

Explain Your Thinking

1 See how Katie coloured the shape to show a fraction.

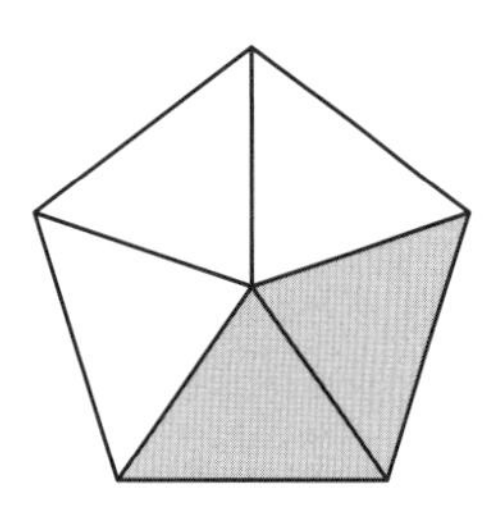

Katie drew and coloured another shape to show the same fraction. Which shape did Katie draw?

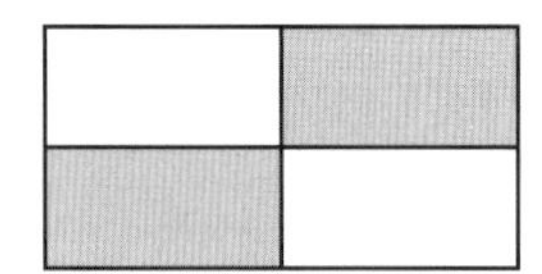

○ 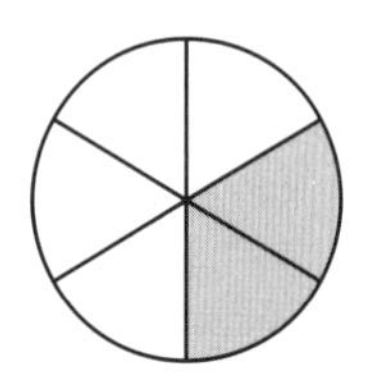

○ 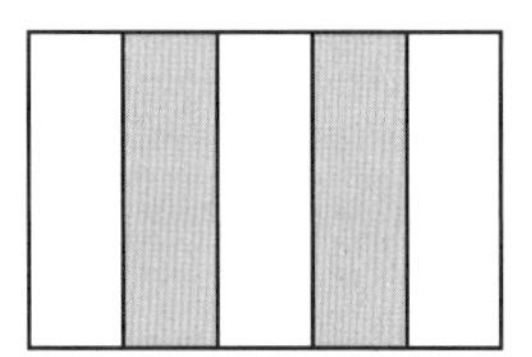

○ 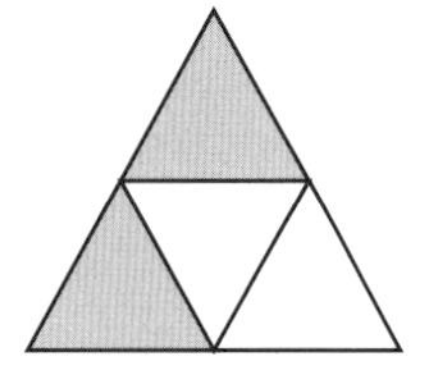

2 Jane caught 135 fish. Eric caught 72 more fish than Jane. If Eric sold 96 of the fish he caught, how many fish would he have left?

○ 111

○ 159

○ 245

○ 303

3 Which number sentence does not belong to the fact family of the addition sentence below?

$$36 + 28 = 64$$

○ 28 + 36 = 64

○ 36 – 28 = 8

○ 64 – 36 = 28

○ 64 – 28 = 36

4 Uncle Tim draws his hammer on a grid.

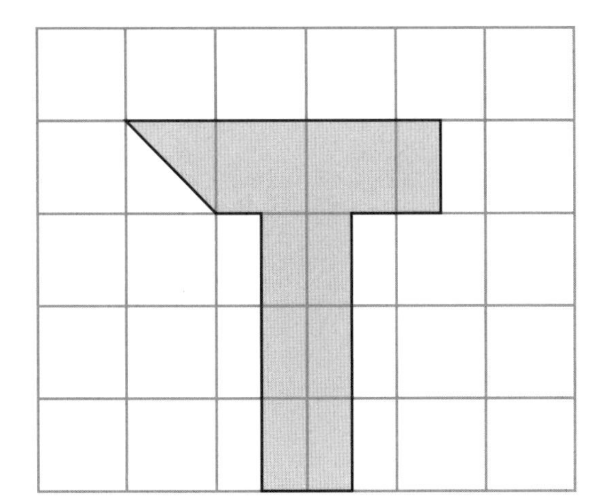

What is the area covered by the hammer in square units?

- ○ 5
- ○ 6
- ○ 7
- ○ 8

5 Which set of measurements is in order from longest to shortest?

- ○ 80 cm, 7 m, 900 cm, 20 km
- ○ 2700 m, 110 m, 18 mm, 2 cm
- ○ 2800 mm, 1300 mm, 60 m, 20 cm
- ○ 7 km, 2600 m, 2 km, 300 cm

6 How many vertices are there in a hexagonal pyramid?

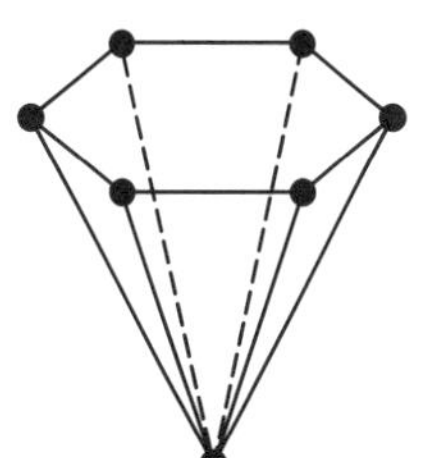

- ○ 6
- ○ 7
- ○ 10
- ○ 12

7 If half of a watermelon weighs 4 kg, what is the weight of a quarter of the watermelon in kilograms?

- ○ 2
- ○ 4
- ○ 6
- ○ 8

8 Look at the pattern.

50, ____ , 100, 125, 150

What is the missing number?

- ○ 60
- ○ 75
- ○ 90
- ○ 110

5

9 Put the following fractions in order from least to greatest:

one half, two thirds, three fourths, two fifths

Use the given diagrams to support your answer.

Explain Your Thinking

10 It takes Danny 45 minutes to finish his dinner every day. The clock below shows the time that Danny finished his dinner today.

What time did Danny start having his dinner?

Explain your answer with the help of the given clock.

Explain Your Thinking

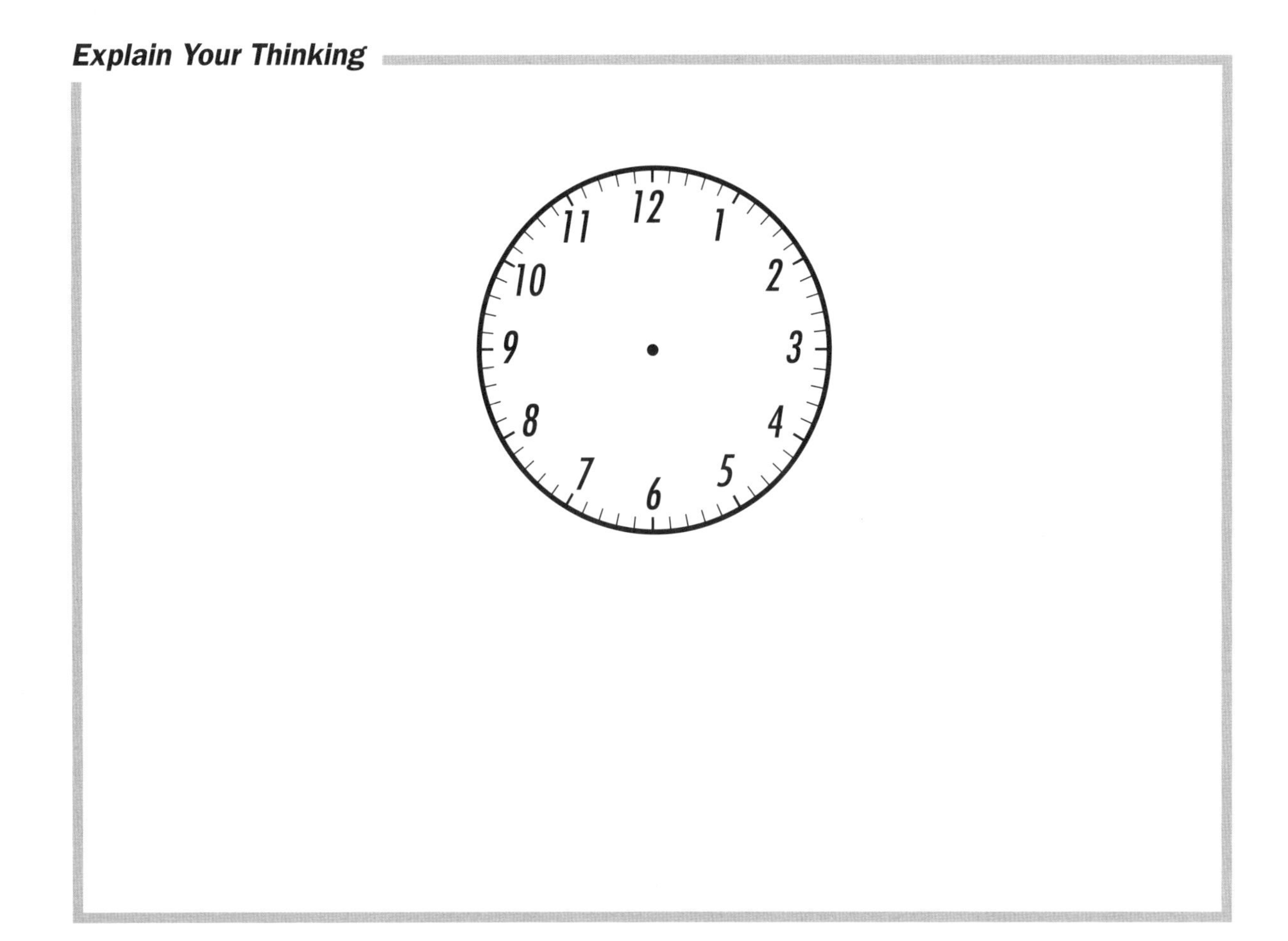

1 How long is the shortest route from City A to City C?

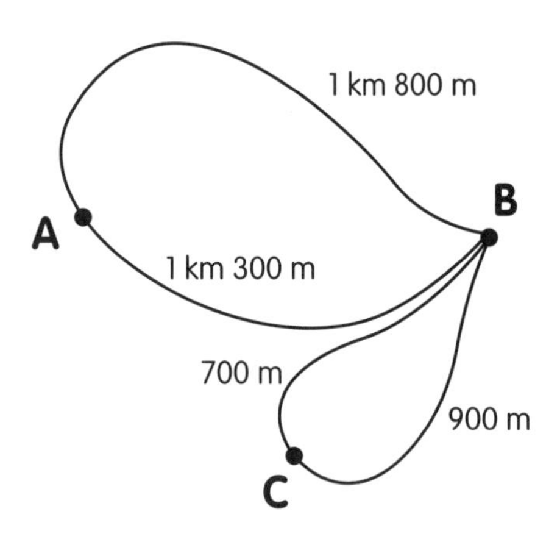

- ○ 2000 km
- ○ 2 km
- ○ 2200 m
- ○ 1800 m

2 What is the answer in expanded form to the vertical addition below?

$$\begin{array}{r} 486 \\ +\ 371 \\ \hline \end{array}$$

- ○ 700 + 50 + 7
- ○ 800 + 50 + 7
- ○ 800 + 60 + 8
- ○ 800 + 70 + 8

3 Look at the objects on the balances.

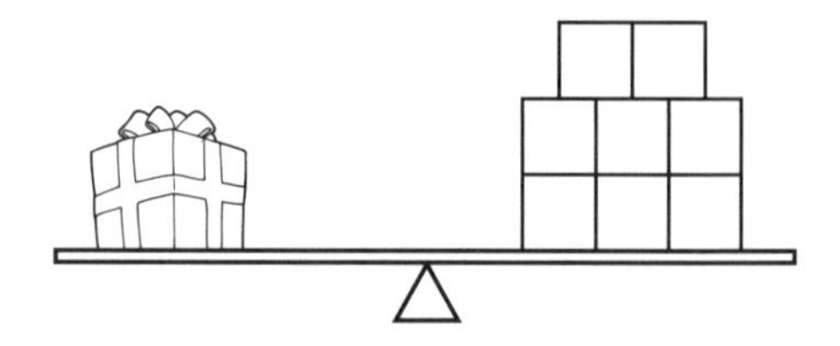

How many frogs have the same weight as a gift?

- ○ 2
- ○ 3
- ○ 4
- ○ 6

4 Which subtraction sentence is related to the number sentence below?

21 + 7 = 28

- ○ 21 – 7 = 14
- ○ 28 – 7 = 21
- ○ 49 – 21 = 28
- ○ 28 – 11 = 17

5 What transformation does the picture show?

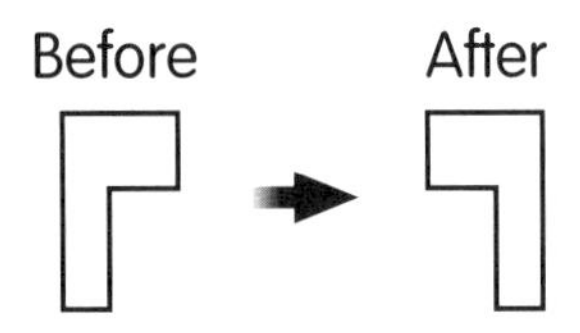

- translation
- rotation
- reflection
- translation and rotation

6 The pictograph shows the number of marbles that John has.

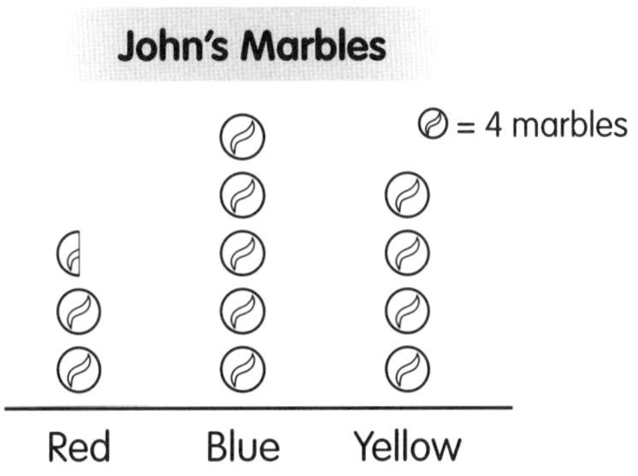

John's Marbles

(marble) = 4 marbles

Red | Blue | Yellow

How many fewer red marbles than blue marbles does John have?

- 10
- 8
- 2
- 12

7 It takes Felix 20 minutes to walk to school. He leaves home at 7:45 a.m. every day. What time does he arrive at school?

- 7:25 a.m.
- 8:05 p.m.
- 8:05 a.m.
- 8:15 a.m.

8 Which line is closest to 4 cm?

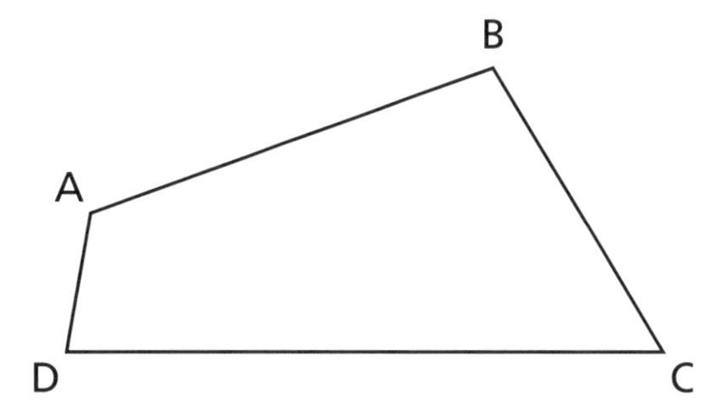

- line AB
- line BC
- line CD
- line AD

9 Jason did a survey on his class about their favourite sports. He used a bar graph to show the data.

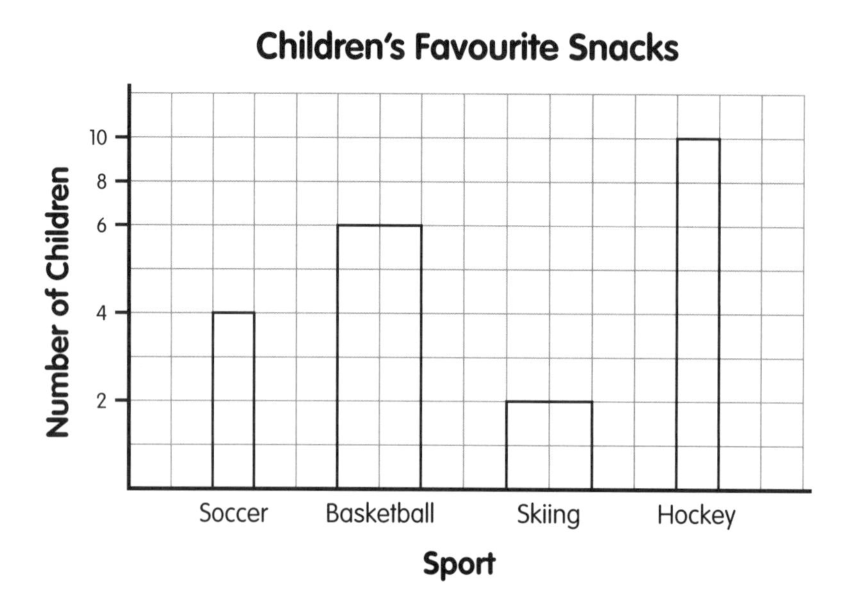

There are 3 mistakes on his graph.

List out the mistakes and draw a correct bar graph.

Show Your Work

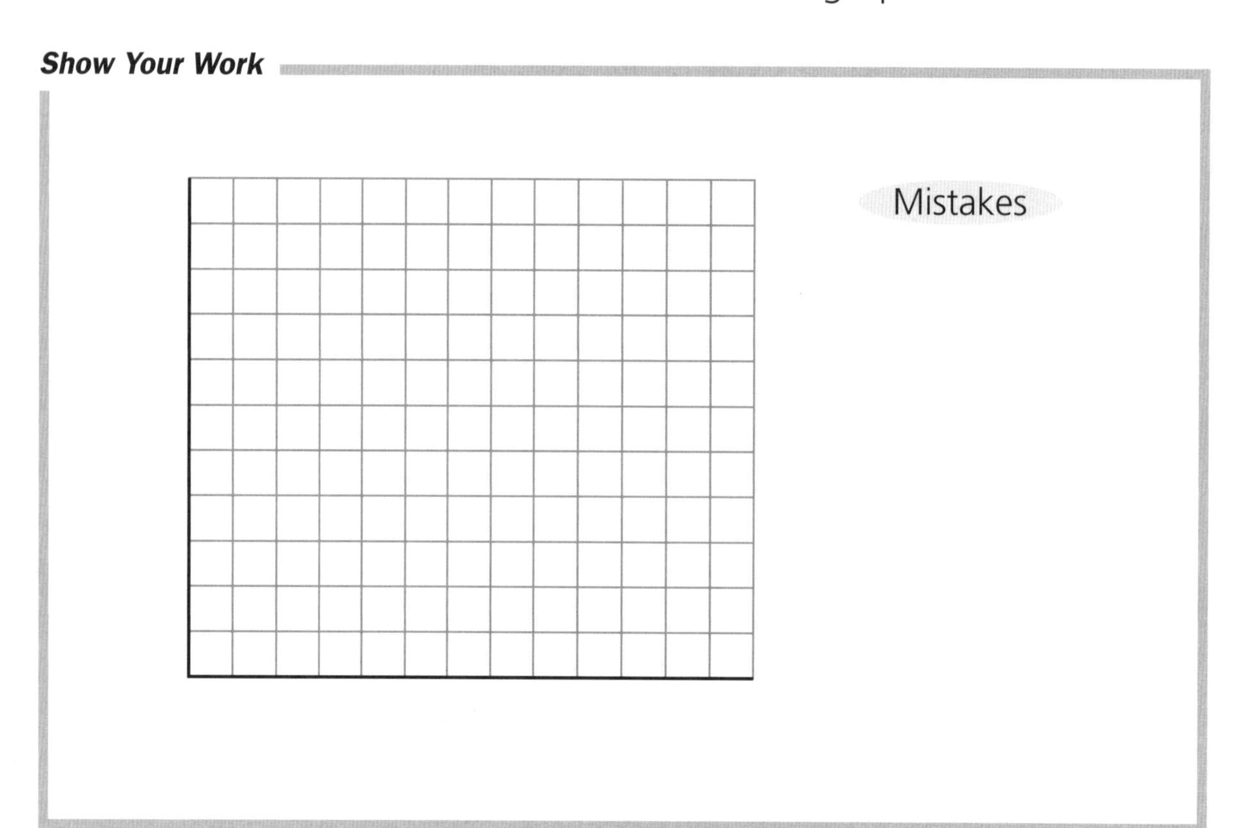

10 Annie goes 2 units up and 4 units left to arrive at the library.

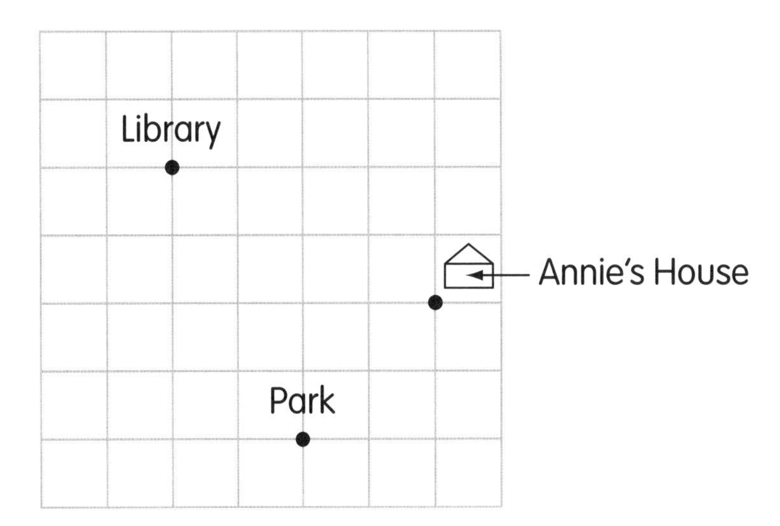

How should Annie go now to get to the park? Then how should Annie go back home from the park?

Show Your Work

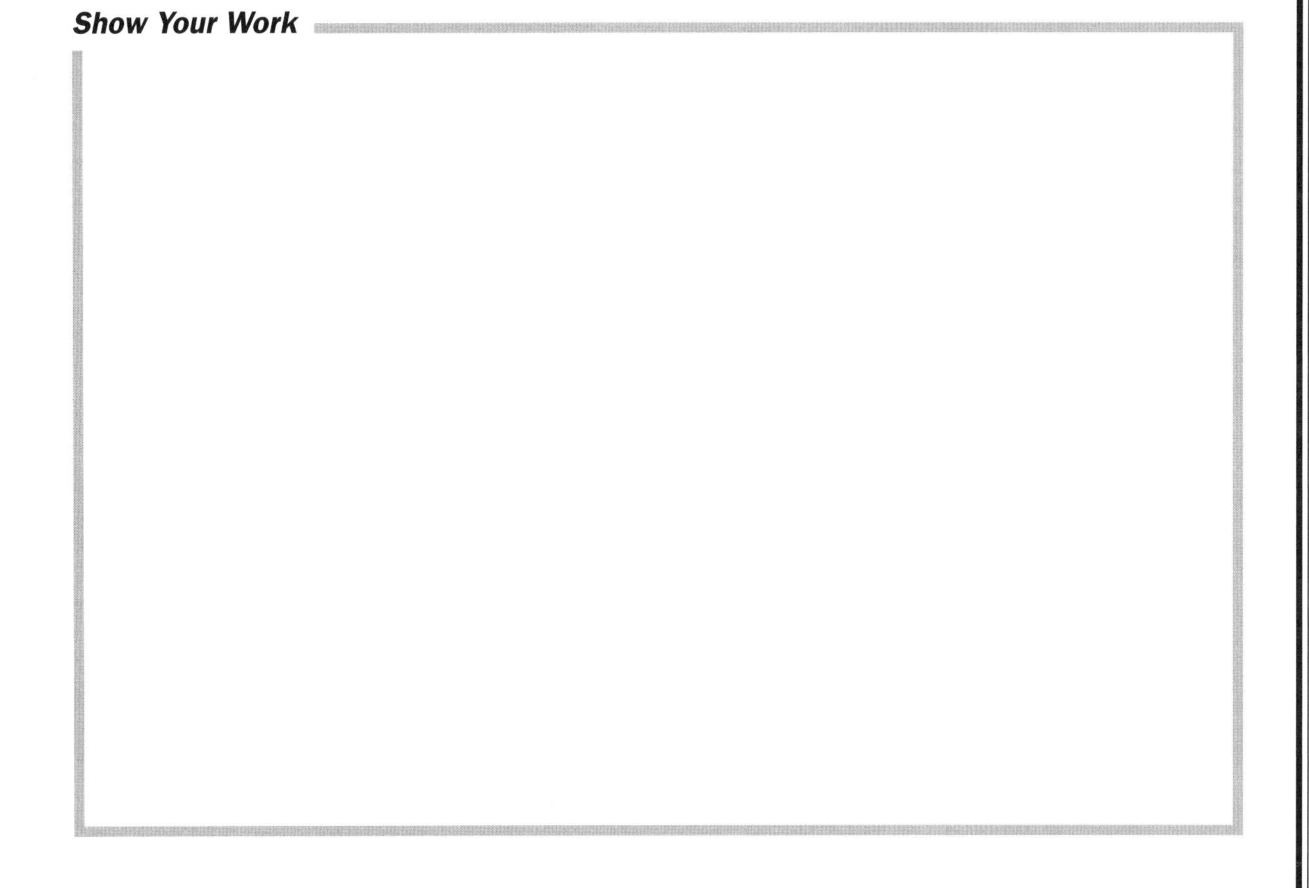

1 Which sentence about the 3-D figures below is true?

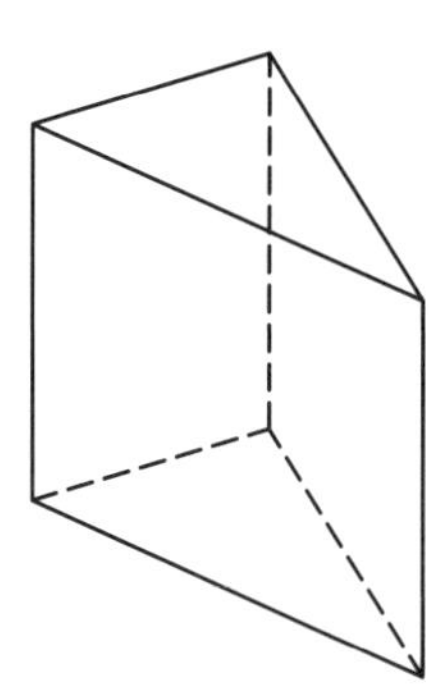
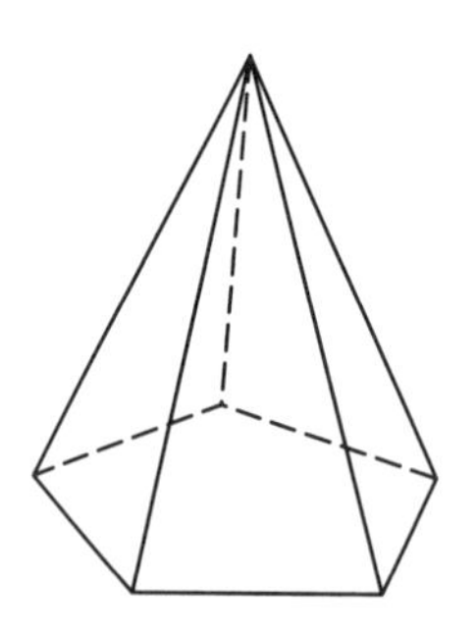

○ Both have 5 faces.
○ The number of vertices that they have are different.
○ Both have triangular faces.
○ Both have 10 edges.

2 How many even numbers are there between 293 and 317?

○ 10
○ 11
○ 12
○ 13

3 Olivia drinks 250 mL of orange juice every day. She wants to find the amount of juice she drinks in 25 days. Which number sentence should she use?

○ $250 \div 50$
○ $25 + 250$
○ 25×250
○ $250 - 25$

4 Look at the Venn diagram.

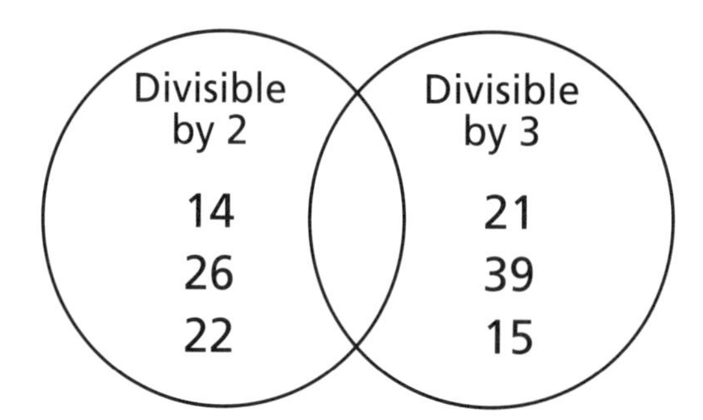

Which number below belongs to the overlapping part?

○ 16
○ 27
○ 42
○ 49

5 The estimate to the vertical addition below is 500.

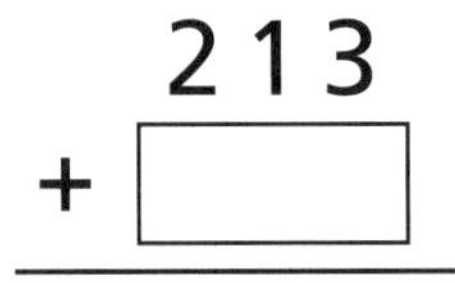

Which is the possible missing number?

- O 364
- O 196
- O 283
- O 227

6 Carol spins the spinner at a game fair. She will win a doll if it lands on red.

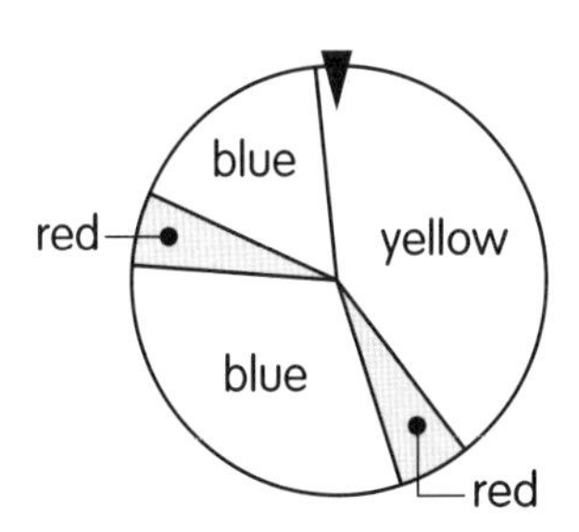

What is the best word to describe the chance that Carol will win a doll?

- O certain
- O unlikely
- O likely
- O impossible

7 Which solid can be formed by the net?

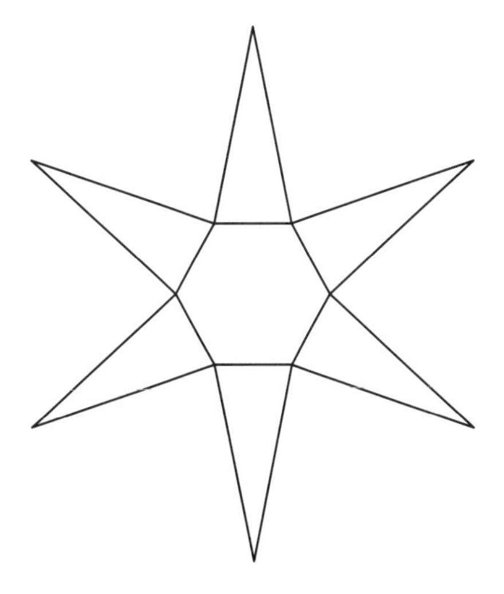

- O hexagonal prism
- O rectangular pyramid
- O pentagonal pyramid
- O hexagonal pyramid

8 How many quarters can trade a toonie?

- O 2
- O 4
- O 8
- O 20

9 Jack has 40 bookmarks and Sue has 28.

Jack gives some of his bookmarks to Sue so that they have the same number of bookmarks.

How many bookmarks does Jack give to Sue?

How many bookmarks does each child have now?

Explain Your Thinking

10 The map shows where David and Jill live. David needs to follow the direction of the arrows to go to Jill's house from his house.

List out all the possible routes that David can take. Then find the distance of taking each route.

What do you notice from the answer?

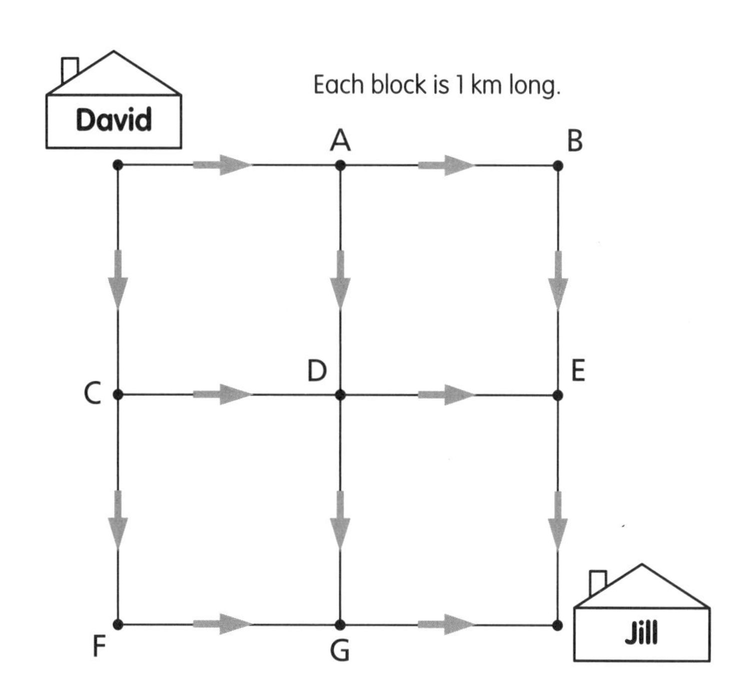

Explain Your Thinking

Possible Routes	Distance Travelled (km)
1. David → A →	

1 Which picture shows a quarter counterclockwise turn of the L-shape?

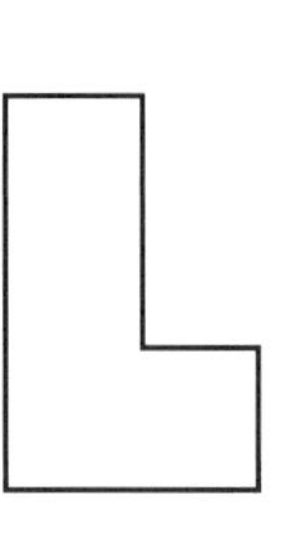

○ 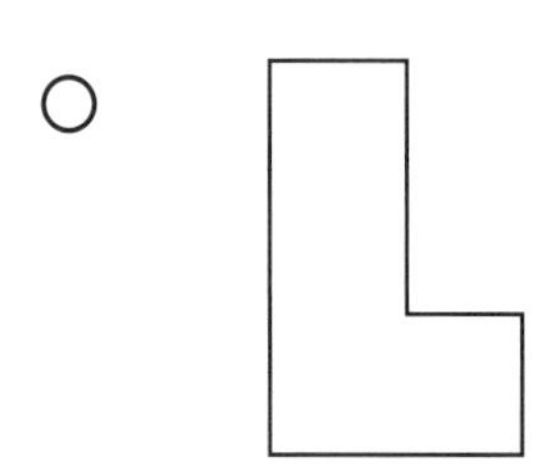

○ 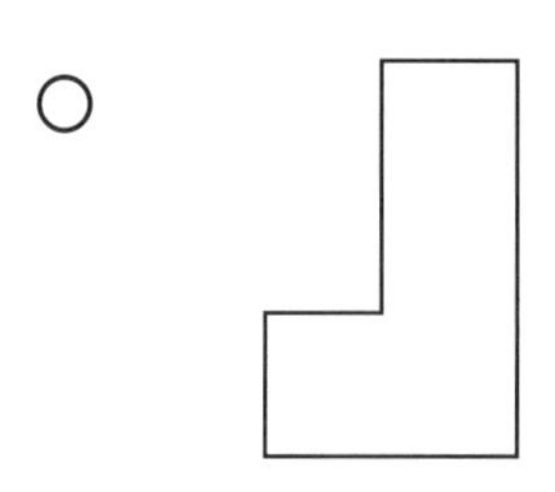

○ 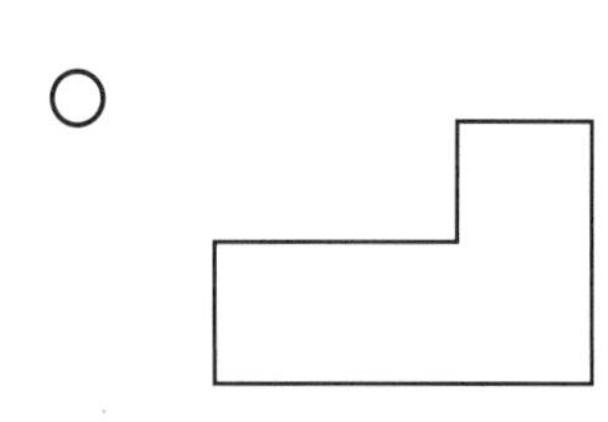

○ 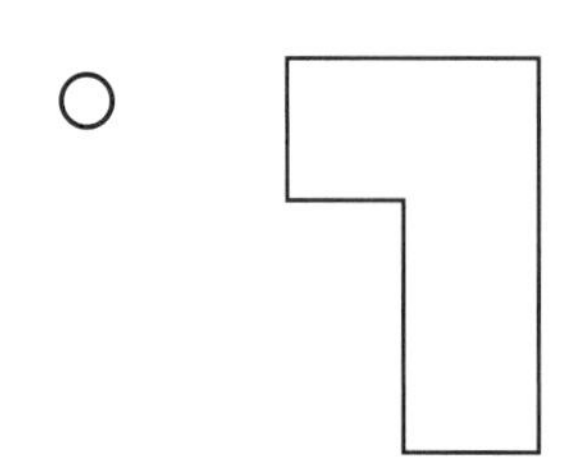

2 The capacity of the container below is one litre.

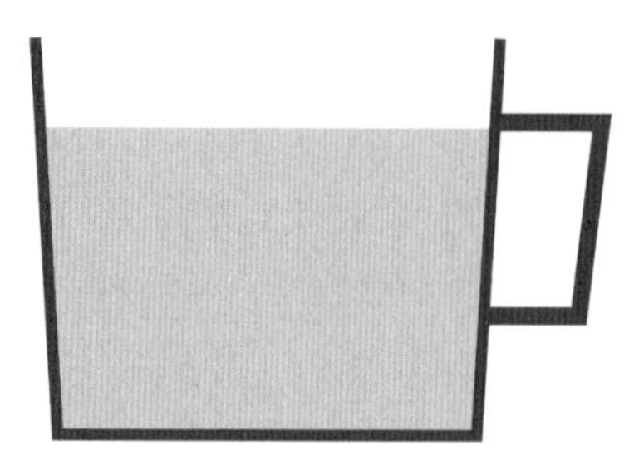

About how much water is in the container now?

○ 1 L
○ half a litre
○ three quarters of a litre
○ one quarter of a litre

3 It takes Aunt Marie 26 days to knit a sweater and 15 days to knit a scarf. About how many weeks does it take her to knit a sweater and a scarf?

○ 6
○ 41
○ 54
○ 287

4 What is the perimeter of a regular octagon with a side length of 5 cm?

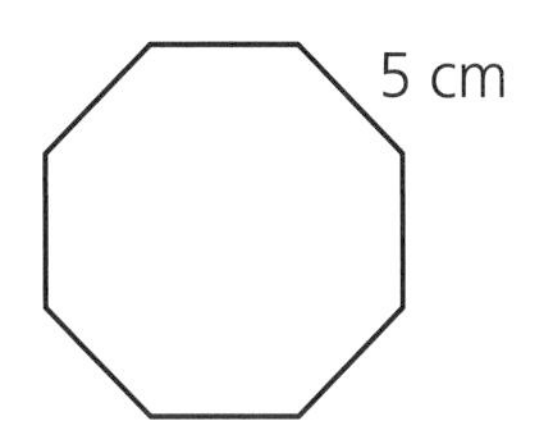

- 8 cm
- 25 cm
- 30 cm
- 40 cm

5 How can ☆ be moved to ☾ on the grid?

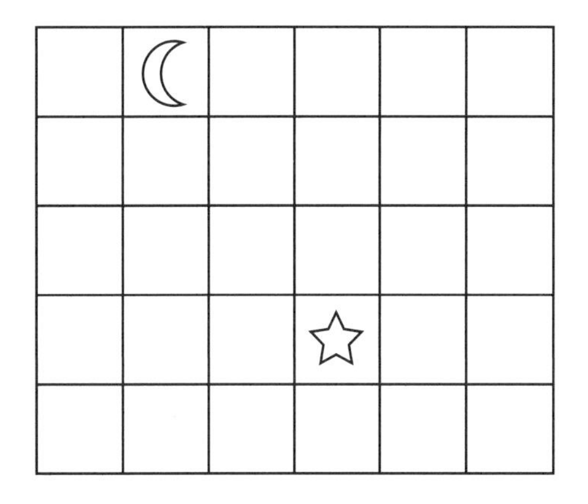

- 2 units left, 3 units up
- 3 units left, 2 units up
- 2 units right, 3 units down
- 3 units right, 2 units down

6 The graph shows the number of storybooks the children have read.

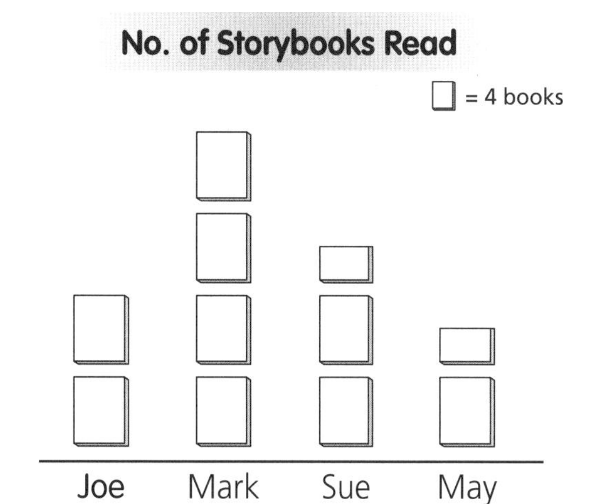

How many storybooks have the girls read in all?

- 6
- 9
- 12
- 16

7 Bob started working on his project on May 16, 2006 and finished it on June 2, 2007. How long did it take Bob to finish his project?

- about 1 week
- about 2 weeks
- about 1 year
- about 2 years

8

8 Look at Linda's number pattern.

Linda's number pattern: 3, 7, 6, 10, 9, 13

Make two number patterns using Linda's pattern rule:

1. Start with "1" and write the next 5 terms.
2. Start with your own number and write the next 4 terms.

Show Your Work

9 Aunt Katie wants to build a rectangular flower bed which has an area of 6 square units.

Find two possible ways of building the flower bed. Draw them on the grid.

If Aunt Katie wants to use less fencing for the flower bed, which dimensions should she choose?

1 square unit

Explain Your Thinking

1 Which solid is described by the sentences below?

- **It has 5 vertices.**
- **It has 5 faces.**
- **It has 4 triangular faces.**
- **It has 1 rectangular face.**

○ triangular prism
○ rectangular pyramid
○ rectangular prism
○ pentagonal prism

2 Tony is tossing a cube that is labelled 1 to 6 on each face. What is the probability that he will get a 3 or 4?

○ 1 in 6
○ 2 in 6
○ 4 in 6
○ 6 in 6

3 What fraction of the square is not shaded?

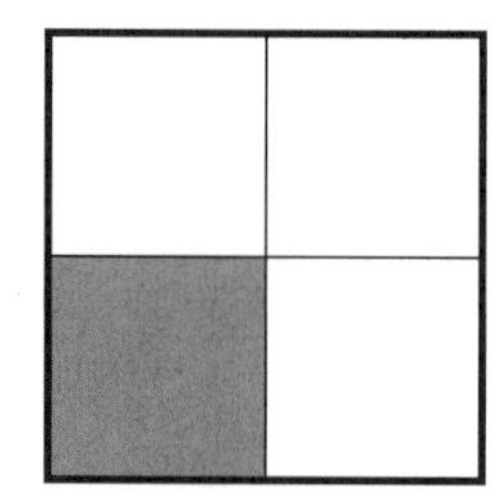

○ one half
○ one fourth
○ three thirds
○ three fourths

4 What is the area of the shape below in square units?

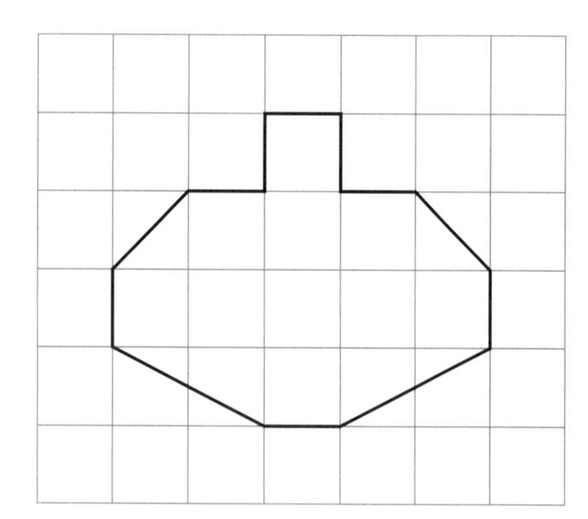

○ 16
○ 15
○ 14
○ 13

5 The graph shows the number of ice cream cones sold yesterday.

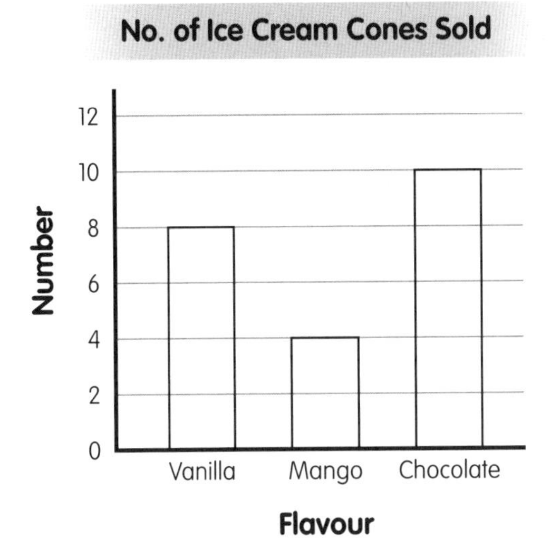

How many ice cream cones were sold yesterday?

- ○ 9
- ○ 11
- ○ 18
- ○ 22

6 What is the time elapsed from 7:55 p.m. to 8:35 p.m.?

- ○ 30 minutes
- ○ 40 minutes
- ○ 1 hour 20 minutes
- ○ 1 hour 40 minutes

7 Janet measured and wrote, "My book is 25 thick." Which measuring unit is missing from the sentence?

- ○ millimetres
- ○ centimetres
- ○ metres
- ○ kilometres

8 Each box has 5 crayons and 2 of them are red. How many red crayons are there in 6 boxes?

- ○ 10
- ○ 12
- ○ 24
- ○ 30

9 Which of the following is best to describe 33 days?

- ○ about 1 week
- ○ about 1 month
- ○ about 3 months
- ○ about 1 year

10 Mrs. Green bought 12 eggs. Unfortunately, one third of the eggs were broken. Mrs. Green used one fourth of the remaining eggs to make cookies.

How many eggs does Mrs. Green have left?

Show your work with the help of pictures.

Explain Your Thinking

11 Janet is drawing symmetrical nets for a 3-D figure.

Help her complete the nets and tell what figure the nets can form.

Show Your Work

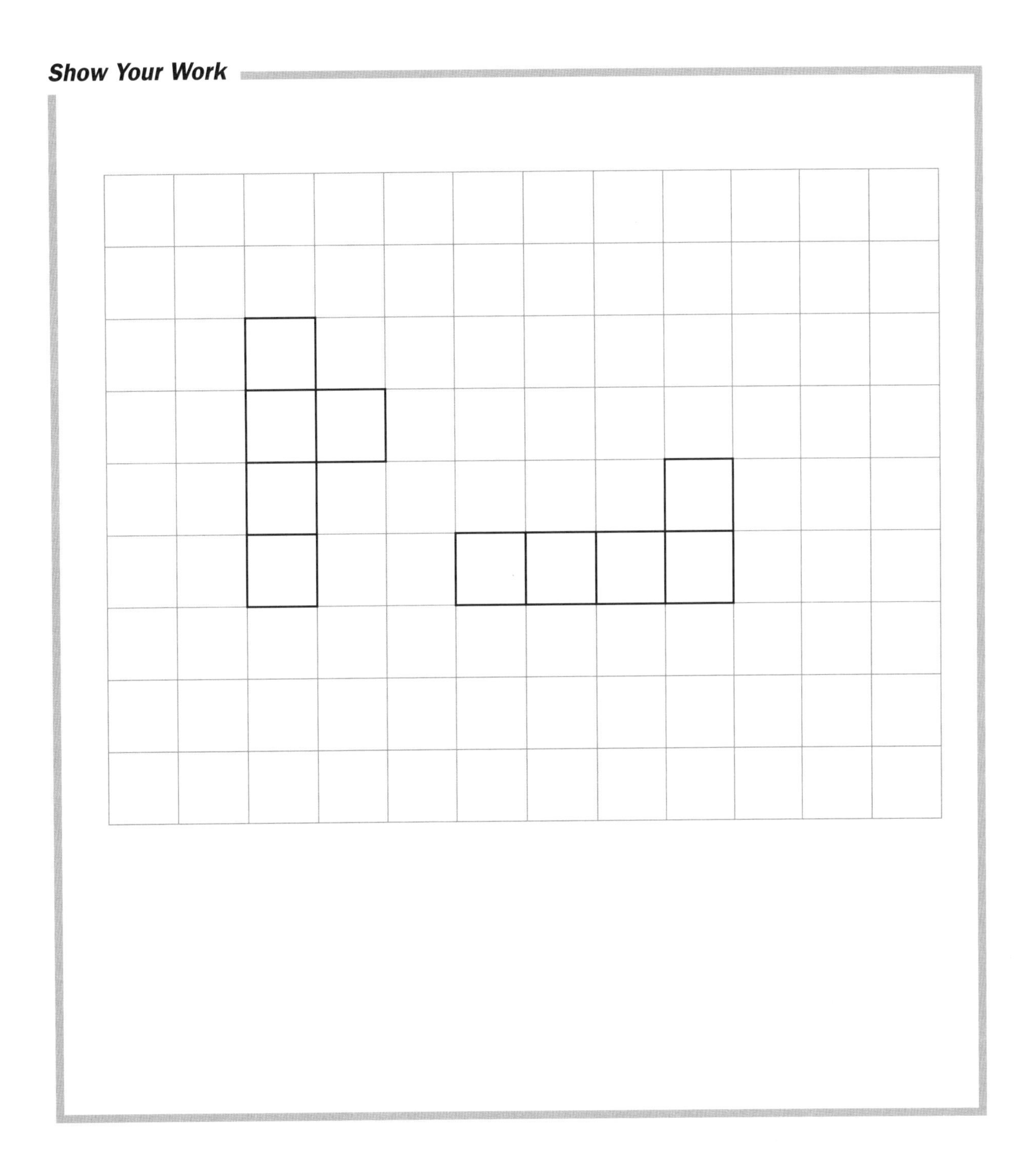

1 How many line(s) of symmetry does the hexagon have?

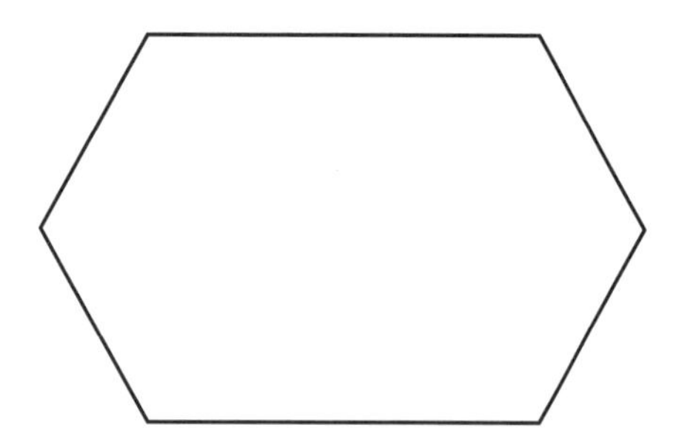

- ○ 0
- ○ 2
- ○ 4
- ○ 6

2 How many numbers between 11 and 28 are divisible by 3?

- ○ 3
- ○ 4
- ○ 5
- ○ 6

3 Which measurement is the longest?

- ○ 20 m
- ○ 6 km
- ○ 70 cm
- ○ 3000 mm

4 Look at Sue's coins.

She wants to buy an ice cream cone which costs 85¢ and pays an extra of 25¢ for adding sprinkles. Which sentence is correct?

- ○ She will have 5¢ left after buying an ice cream cone with sprinkles.
- ○ She will have 10¢ left after buying an ice cream cone with sprinkles.
- ○ She needs 5¢ more to get what she wants.
- ○ She needs 10¢ more to get what she wants.

5 6 fill a .

4 fill a .

How many are needed to fill a ?

- O 4
- O 6
- O 24
- O 36

6 What number does A represent?

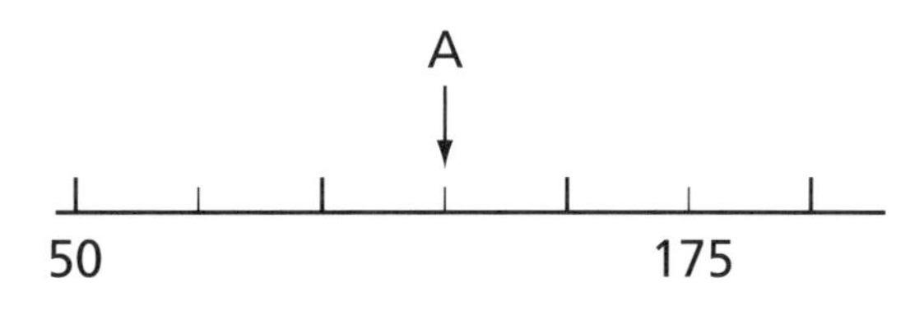

- O 75
- O 125
- O 150
- O 200

7 Look at the pattern.

Figure 1 Figure 2 Figure 3

How many dots will there be in Figure 6?

- O 9
- O 11
- O 13
- O 15

8 The net below makes a rectangular prism.

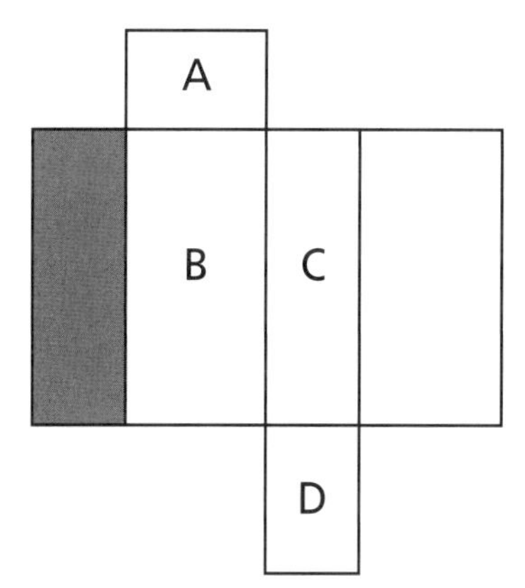

Which face is opposite to the shaded one?

- O A
- O B
- O C
- O D

10

9 Circle 38 on the hundreds chart.

1	2	3	4	5	6	7	8	9	10
11	12	13	14	15	16	17	18	19	20
21	22	23	24	25	26	27	28	29	30
31	32	33	34	35	36	37	38	39	40
41	42	43	44	45	46	47	48	49	50
51	52	53	54	55	56	57	58	59	60
61	62	63	64	65	66	67	68	69	70
71	72	73	74	75	76	77	78	79	80
81	82	83	84	85	86	87	88	89	90
91	92	93	94	95	96	97	98	99	100

Start at 38 and count on by 9's six times. Circle the numbers that you have got on the chart. Describe the pattern of the circled numbers.

Explain Your Thinking

10 Look at the objects below.

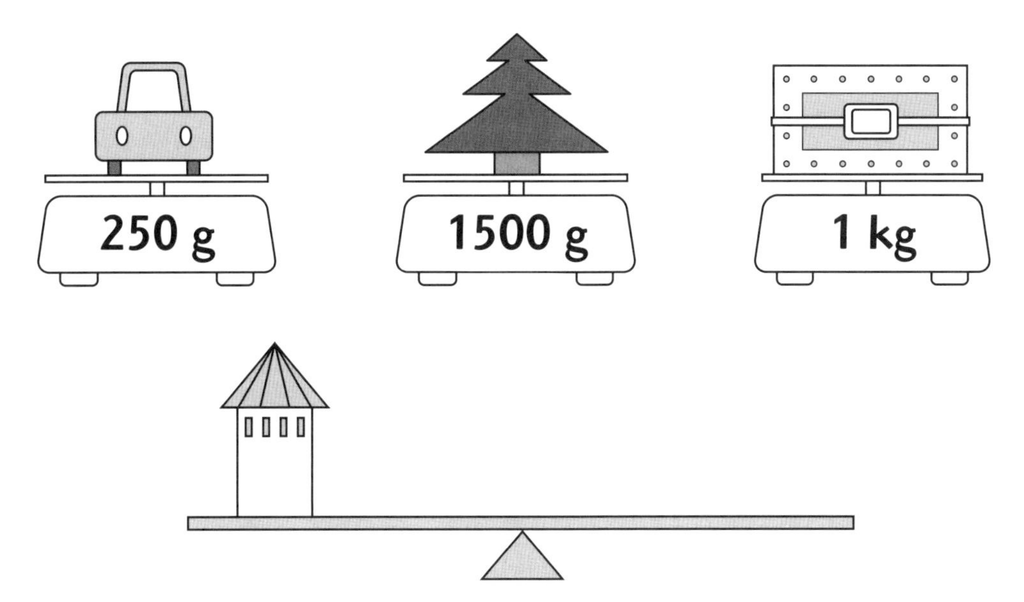

The tower weighs 2 kg. Show 2 different ways to balance the tower using the objects above. You can use each object more than once.

Show your answer with drawings.

Explain Your Thinking

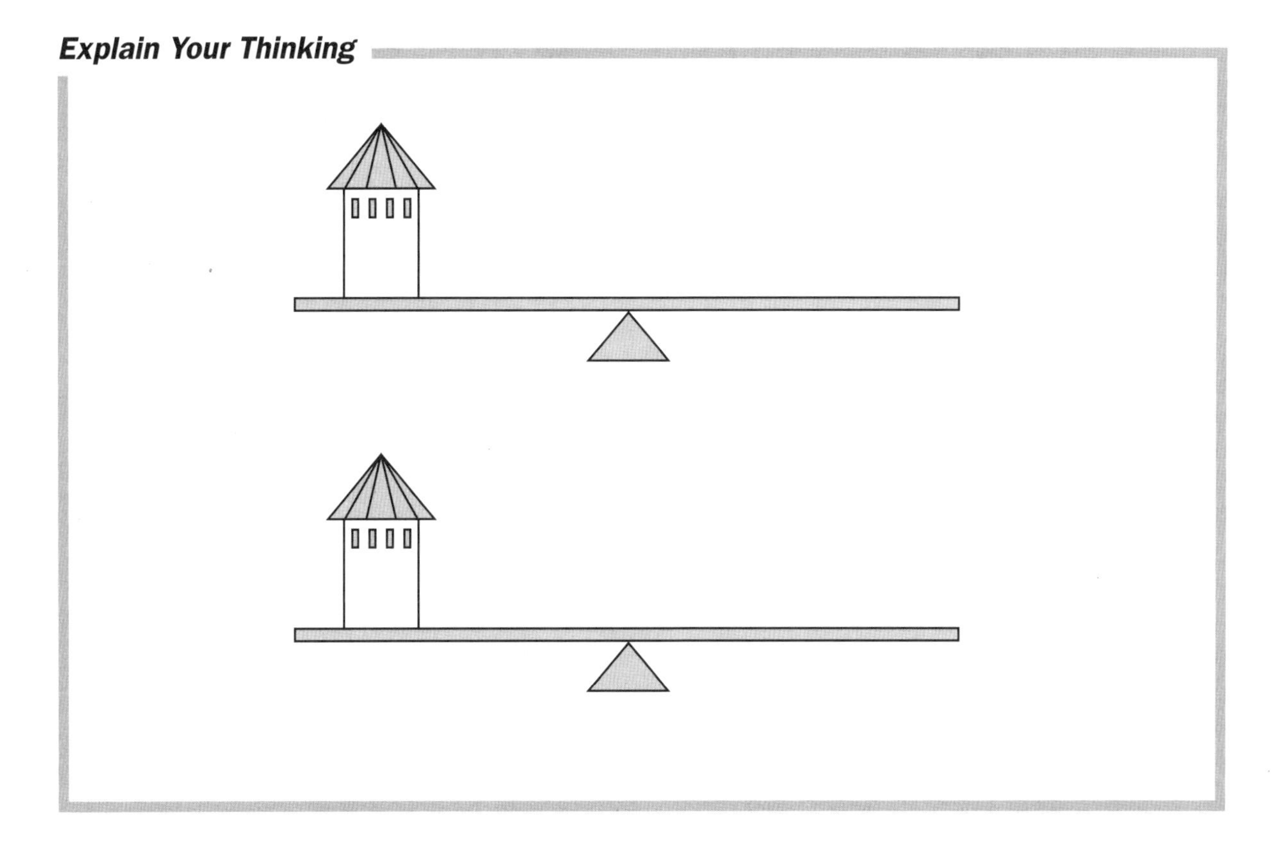

1 Each pizza is cut into 8 slices. How many slices are there in 3 pizzas?

- ○ 16
- ○ 24
- ○ 28
- ○ 32

2 Look at the shapes below.

Which sentence about the shapes is false?

- ○ They have two pairs of equal sides.
- ○ They have two pairs of parallel sides.
- ○ They are quadrilaterals.
- ○ They have exactly one pair of equal angles.

3 Look at the shape below.

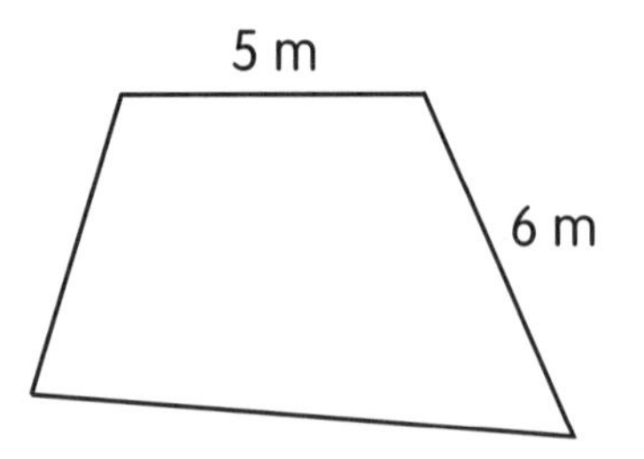

The perimeter of the shape is 25 m. Which set might be the missing lengths?

- ○ 5 m, 9 m
- ○ 6 m, 7 m
- ○ 7 m, 8 m
- ○ 14 m, 14 m

4 Look at the pattern.

$1 + 7 = 8$
$2 + 6 = 8$
$3 + 5 = 8$

Which number sentence comes next?

- ○ $5 + 3 = 8$
- ○ $4 + 4 = 8$
- ○ $8 + 3 = 11$
- ○ $8 - 5 = 3$

5 Look at the diagram.

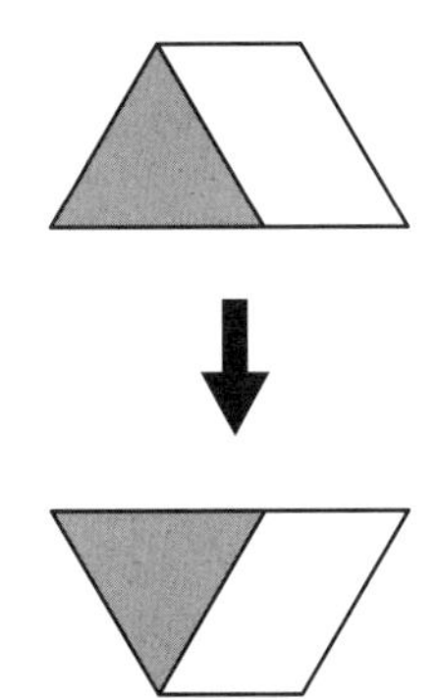

What transformation does it show?

- ○ rotation
- ○ reflection
- ○ circulation
- ○ translation

6 A can fill 4 . Each can hold 250 mL of water.

What is the capacity of a ?

- ○ 500 mL
- ○ 1 L
- ○ 1000 L
- ○ 2000 mL

7 Mrs. Karr gives an assignment to her class on June 22 and says, "This assignment is due in 2 weeks." On what date is the assignment due?

June						
S	M	T	W	T	F	S
					1	2
3	4	5	6	7	8	9
10	11	12	13	14	15	16
17	18	19	20	21	22	23
24	25	26	27	28	29	30

- ○ June 8
- ○ June 15
- ○ July 5
- ○ July 6

8 Celine paid $5 for a sandwich which cost $3.35. The cashier gave her the change with the fewest coins. How many coins were there?

- ○ 2
- ○ 3
- ○ 5
- ○ 7

9 Janet has 6 cards each labelled "1", "2", and "3". She shuffles the cards and draws one card each time.

Look at the results of her 30 draws.

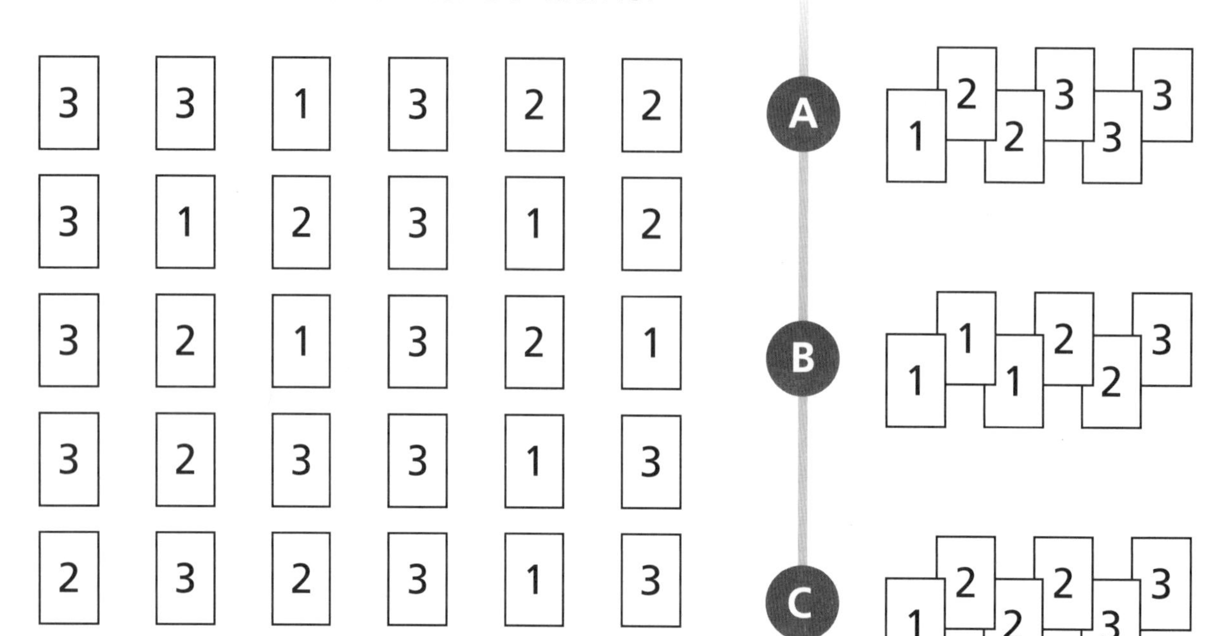

Complete the tally chart. Guess which set of cards Janet might have.

Explain your choice.

Explain Your Thinking

Card Number	Tally
1	
2	
3	

10 Pizza A was cut into 8 equal slices and Pizza B was cut into 6 equal slices.

Uncle Sam ate 5 slices of Pizza A.

Uncle Tom ate 4 slices of Pizza B.

Uncle Sam says, "I've eaten more pizza than Tom."

Is he correct? Complete and label the diagrams to help explain your thinking.

Explain Your Thinking

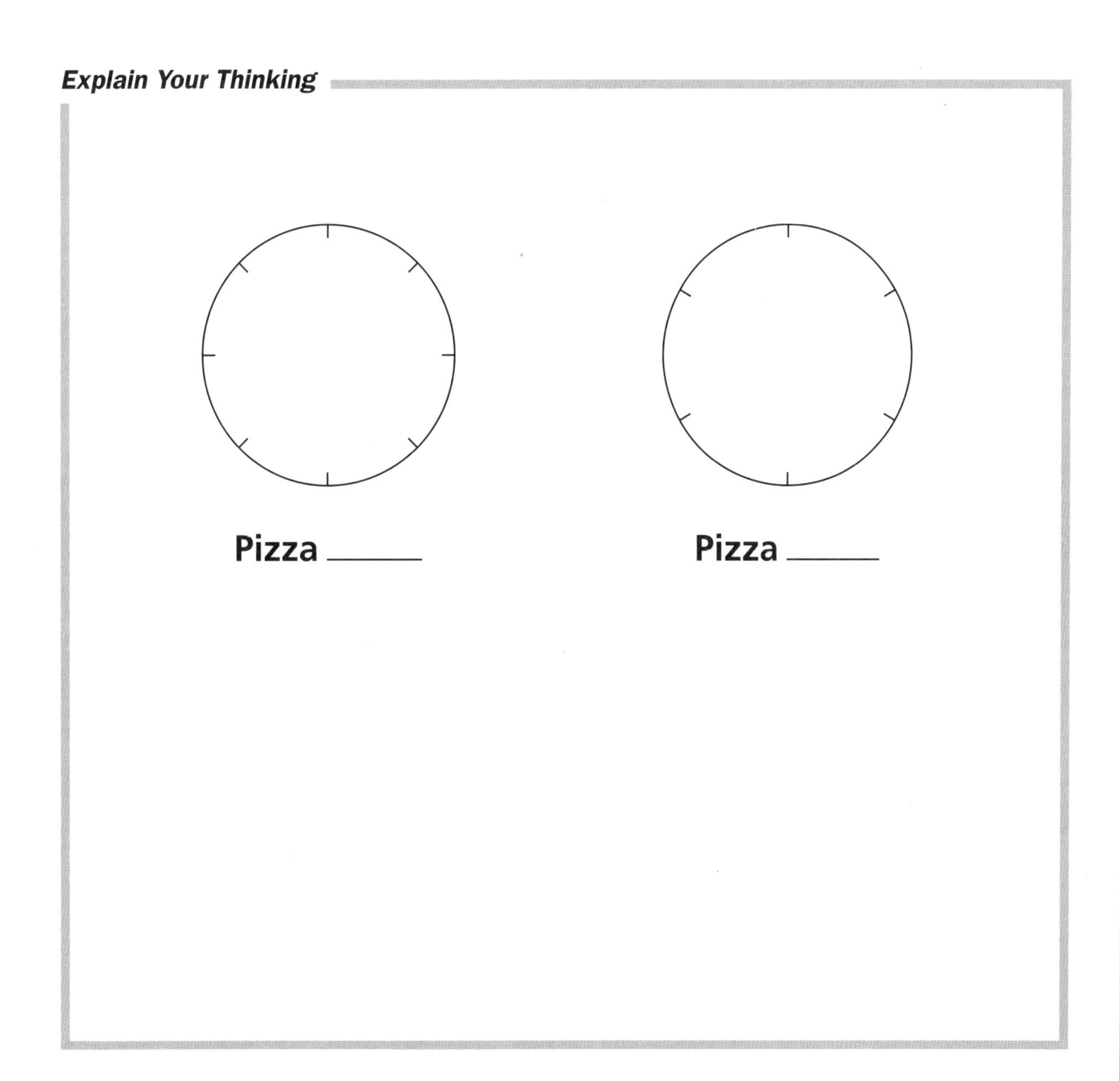

1 Tom's mother gives Tom $3 every week. How long will it take Tom to save $12 if he spends $1 a week?

- O 4 weeks
- O 6 weeks
- O 10 days
- O 12 days

2 Ashley is finding the missing number in the multiplication sentence below.

$$7 \times \square = 42$$

Which related fact can she use to find the missing number?

- O $42 \div 6 = 7$
- O $42 - 7 = 35$
- O $7 + 35 = 42$
- O $42 \times 7 = 294$

3 Kevin has a bag of 20 apples. 5 of them are golden, 3 are green, and the rest are red. What fraction of the apples is red?

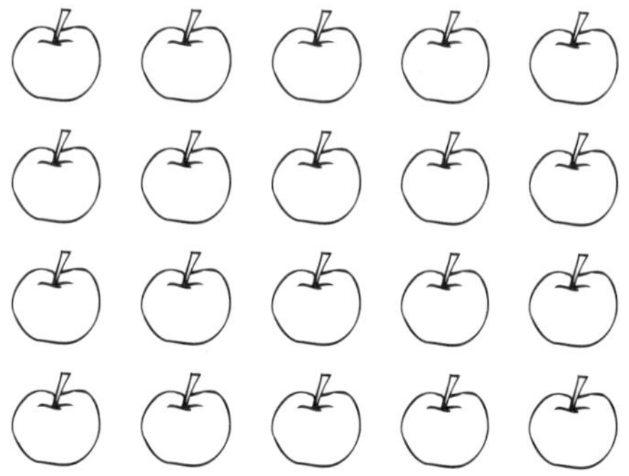

- O $\frac{4}{20}$
- O $\frac{8}{20}$
- O $\frac{12}{20}$
- O $\frac{16}{20}$

4 Ann shares 24 marbles equally with 2 friends. How many marbles does each child get?

- O 3
- O 4
- O 8
- O 12

5 What fraction of the circle is shaded?

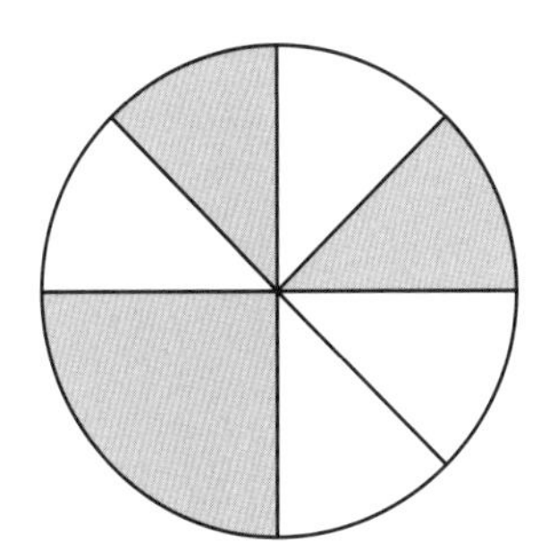

- $\frac{3}{7}$
- $\frac{3}{4}$
- $\frac{3}{8}$
- $\frac{4}{8}$

6 Cathy wants to paint all the triangular faces of the triangular prism.

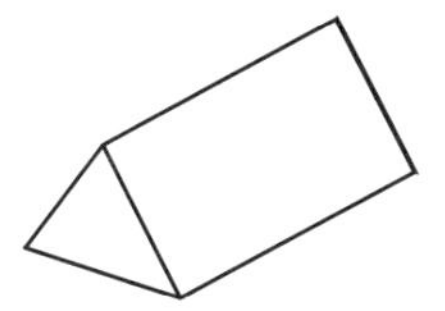

How many faces will be painted?

- 2
- 3
- 4
- 5

7 What is the best word to describe the chance of drawing a ★ or ◎ from the box below?

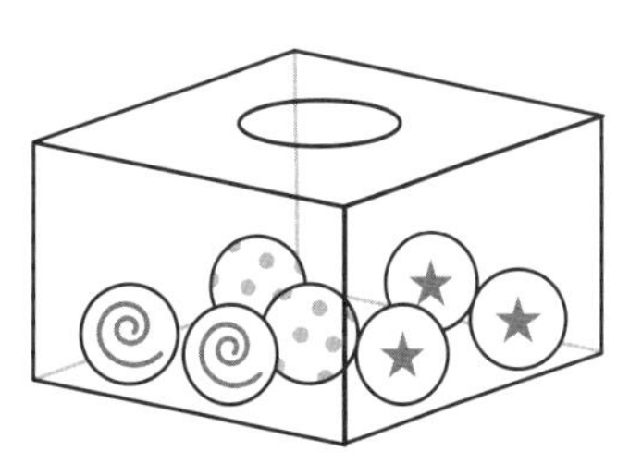

- impossible
- unlikely
- likely
- certain

8 The number of vertices that a pentagonal prism has is 2 times that of a rectangular pyramid.

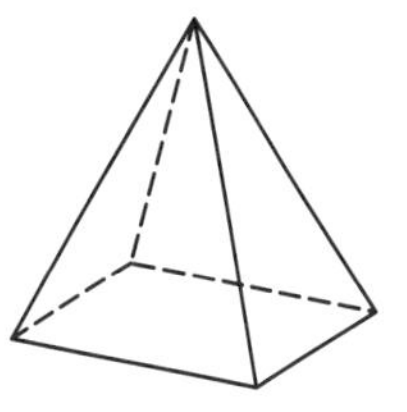

How many vertices does a pentagonal prism have?

- 5
- 7
- 10
- 12

9 Tom walks his dog around a rectangular park.

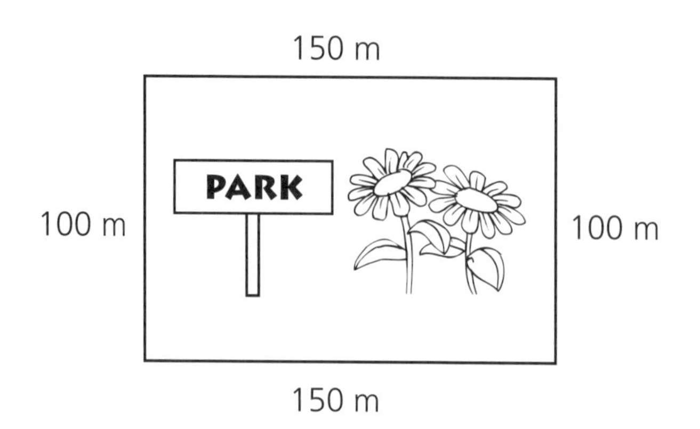

If Tom and his dog walk around the park 3 times, what will be the total distance travelled?

Explain Your Thinking

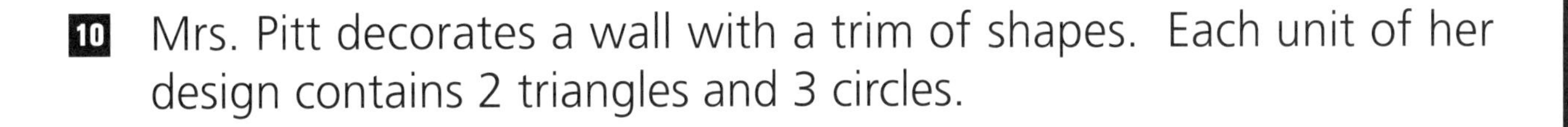

10 Mrs. Pitt decorates a wall with a trim of shapes. Each unit of her design contains 2 triangles and 3 circles.

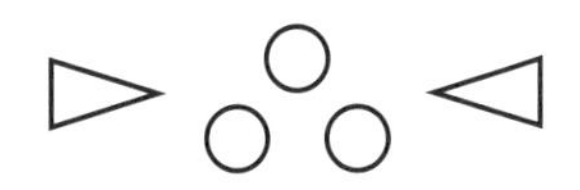

Record the number of each kind of shape in the first four units in the chart.

Following the pattern, how many units can Mrs. Pitt make with 12 triangles?

How many circles are needed to go with 12 triangles?

Explain Your Thinking

Units	Triangles	Circles

1 Draw a card without looking.

1	6	3	10	8
4	2	5	9	7

Which sentence describes the chance of drawing an even number card and the chance of drawing an odd number card?

- ○ There is a better chance of drawing an odd number card.
- ○ It is equally likely to draw an odd number card or an even number card.
- ○ There is a better chance of drawing an even number card.
- ○ It is certain to draw an odd number card and impossible to draw an even number card.

2 Count the number of faces on each figure.

A 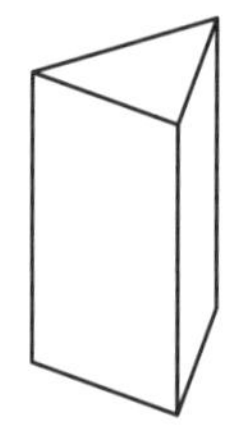

B

C 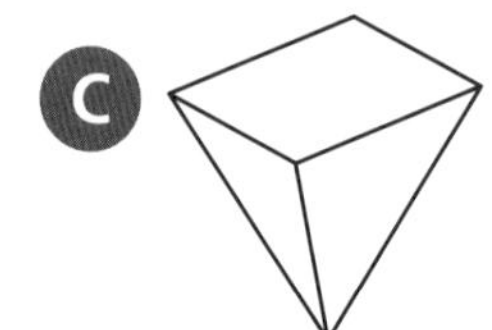

D 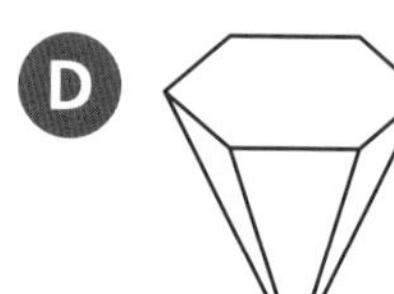

E 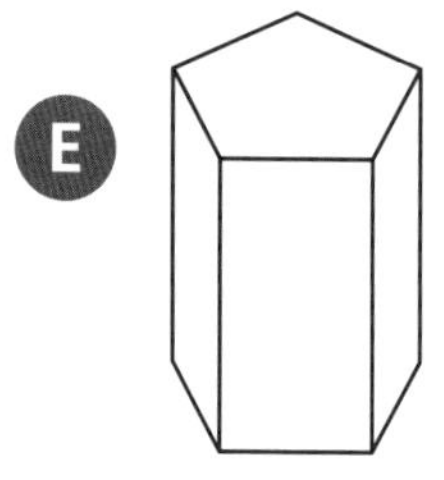

F 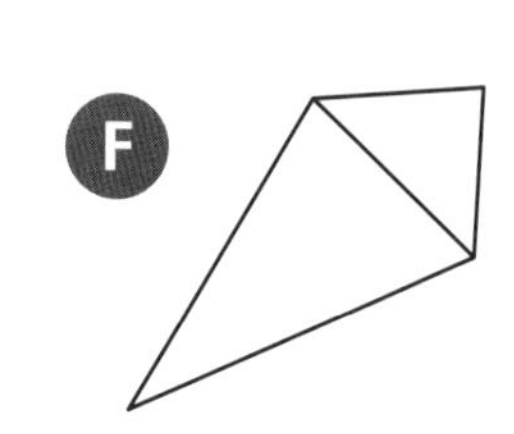

Which set contains the figures that have more than 5 faces?

- ○ A, C, and F
- ○ B, C, and F
- ○ A, C, and E
- ○ B, D, and E

3 Which of the following is another way to show 3 x 5?

- O 5 x 5 x 5
- O 3 + 3 + 3
- O 5 + 5 + 5
- O 3 x 3 x 3

4 Bill has 127 $10 bills, and Connie has 13 fewer $10 bills than Bill does. How many $10 bills does Connie have?

- O 114
- O 140
- O 170
- O 1140

5 Look at the number pattern.

4, 7, 6, 9, 8, 11,...

What is the pattern rule?

- O add 1, subtract 3
- O subtract 3, add 1
- O add 3, subtract 1
- O add 3, subtract 3

6 Which object is in the shape of a cylinder?

O 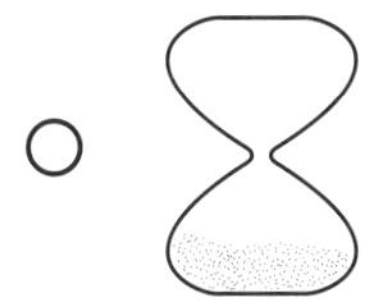

O 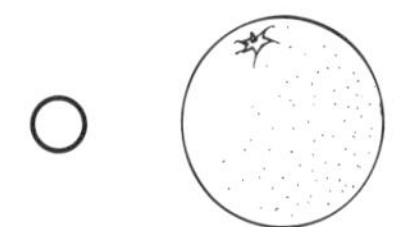

O 

O 

7 The opposite sides of a rectangle are equal in length.

8 cm

2 cm

What is the perimeter of the rectangle?

- O 10 cm
- O 16 cm
- O 18 cm
- O 20 cm

8 The T-shirts in Uncle Sam's Store are in 4 different colours. There are 100 T-shirts in each colour. Below is the number of T-shirts in stock after a week.

	Red	Blue	Orange	Green
No. of T-Shirts in Stock	26	35	19	52

If Uncle Sam orders more T-shirts for next week, should he order the same number of T-shirts of each colour? If not, which colour should he order the most?

Round the data to the nearest ten and draw a horizontal bar graph using the rounded data.

Explain Your Thinking

	Red	Blue	Orange	Green
Rounded Numbers				

9 Follow the rules and sort the numbers in the box into the Venn diagram.

Explain how you sorted the numbers into the overlapping part. Then give one more example in each part of the diagram. Write the example in the circle.

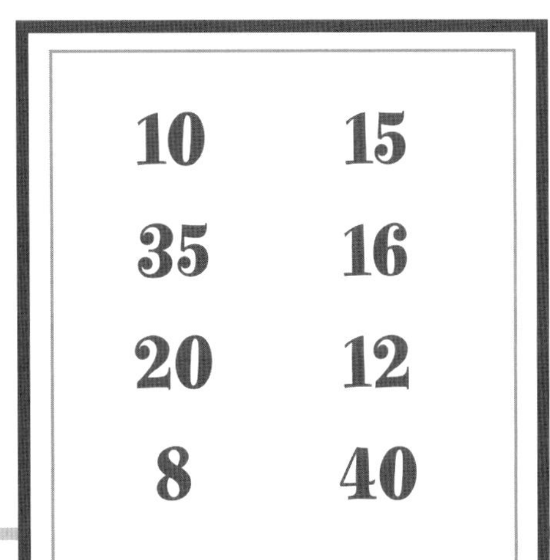

Explain Your Thinking

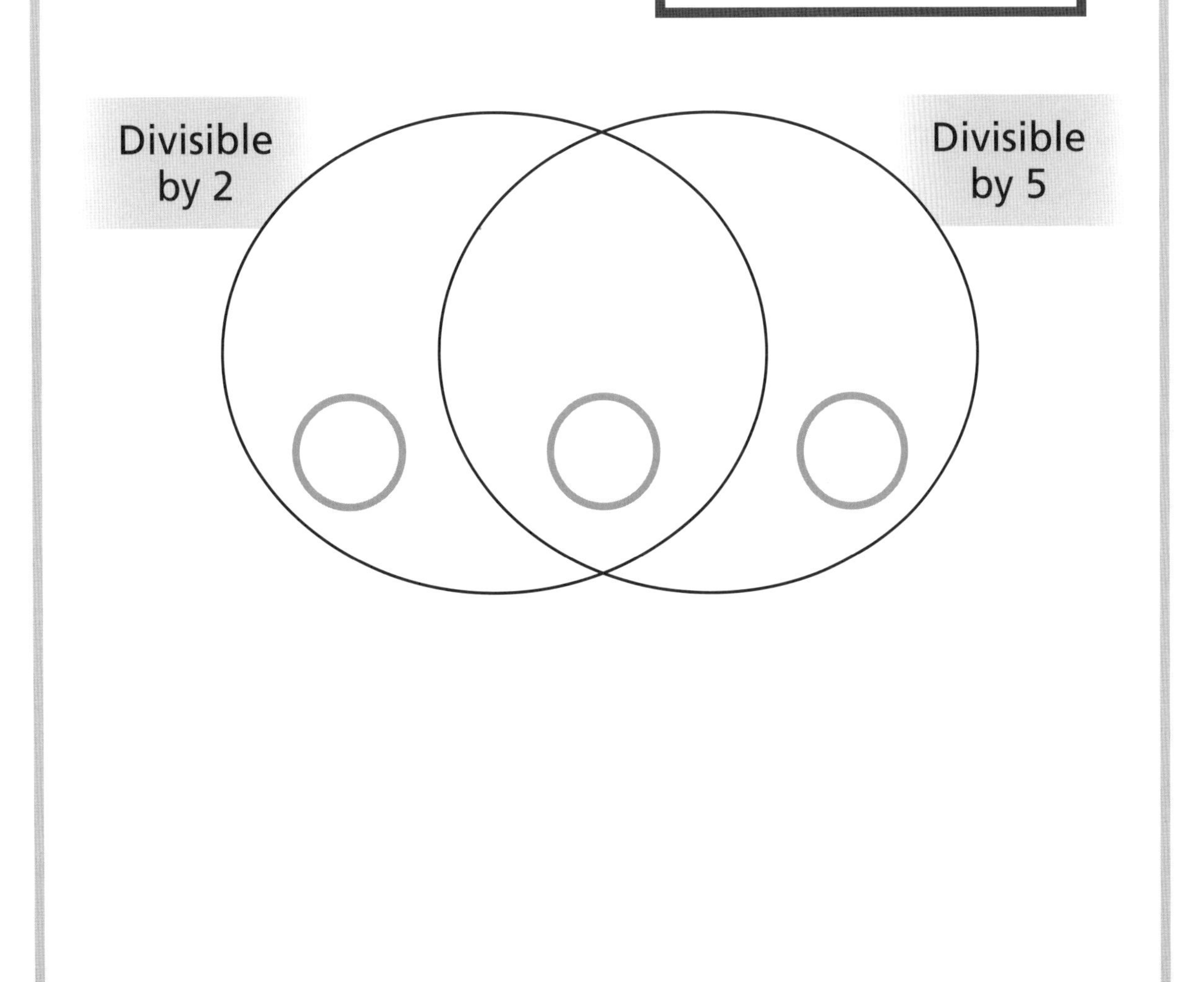

1 Which number pattern has the pattern rule below?

"Multiply by 2 and add 1."

- O 4, 8, 12, 16, 20
- O 1, 4, 10, 22, 46
- O 2, 5, 11, 23, 47
- O 3, 5, 9, 17, 33

2 Look at the Venn Diagram.

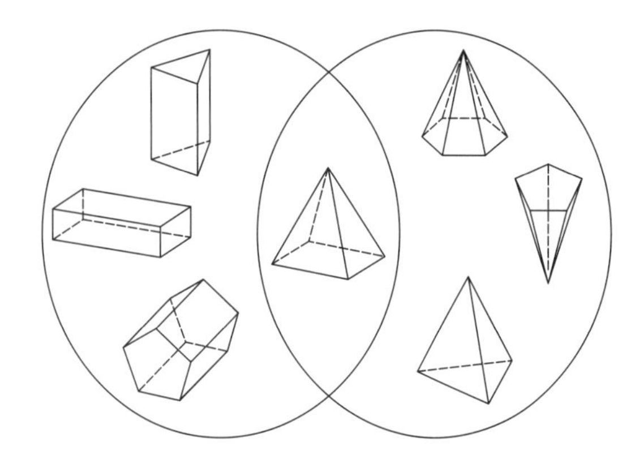

Which rule was used to sort these shapes?

- O prisms and 7 vertices
- O prisms and pyramids
- O 12 edges and triangular faces
- O rectangular faces and pyramids

3 How many squares are there in the diagram below?

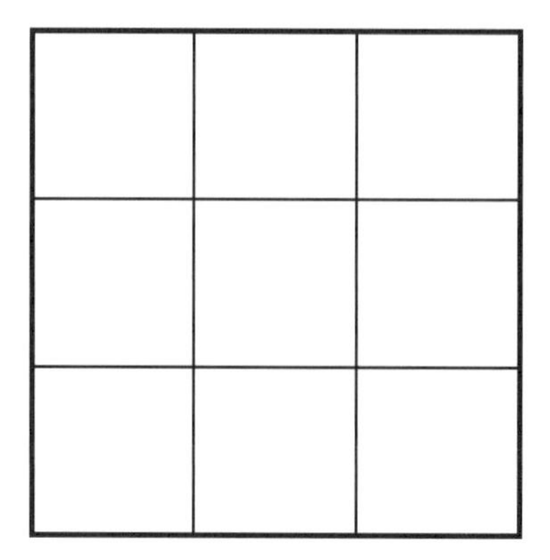

- O 12
- O 13
- O 14
- O 15

4 Nelson is trading the following coins for dimes.

How many dimes can he get?

- O 8
- O 12
- O 15
- O 18

5 It is 11:45 a.m. now. What time will it be after 35 minutes?

- ○ 12:35 p.m.
- ○ 12:00 p.m.
- ○ 12:20 p.m.
- ○ 11:20 a.m.

6 Vincent made the pattern below with arrows.

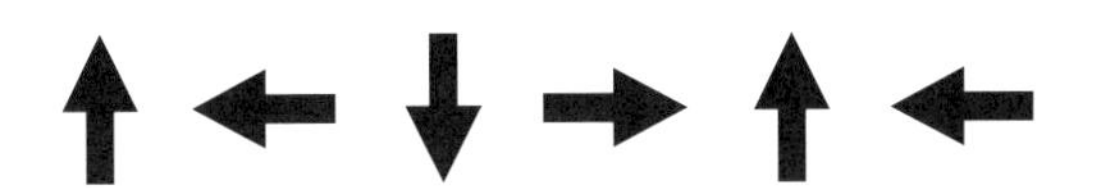

Which sentence best describes the pattern rule?

- ○ The arrow points up and then points to the left.
- ○ The arrow points down each time.
- ○ The arrow makes a $\frac{1}{4}$ counterclockwise turn each time.
- ○ The arrow flips vertically each time.

7 Which of the following could be the temperature of the lemonade in degrees Celsius?

- ○ 45
- ○ 37
- ○ 24
- ○ 4

8 Joseph has 35 cookies. If he puts his cookies equally into 7 boxes, how many cookies are there in each box?

- ○ 7
- ○ 49
- ○ 5
- ○ 35

9 Mrs. Thompson bought 1 bag of chips on Sunday, 2 bags on Monday, 3 bags on Tuesday, and 4 bags on Wednesday.

If she follows this pattern to buy chips, how many bags of chips will she buy on Thursday, Friday, and Saturday?

How many bags of chips will she buy in a week?

Explain Your Thinking

10 The children are going to spin the spinner below 60 times. Each child has made a prediction on the result.

Children	No. of Times		
	Red	**Green**	**Blue**
Lisa	32	19	9
Brian	14	16	30
Cindy	12	19	29

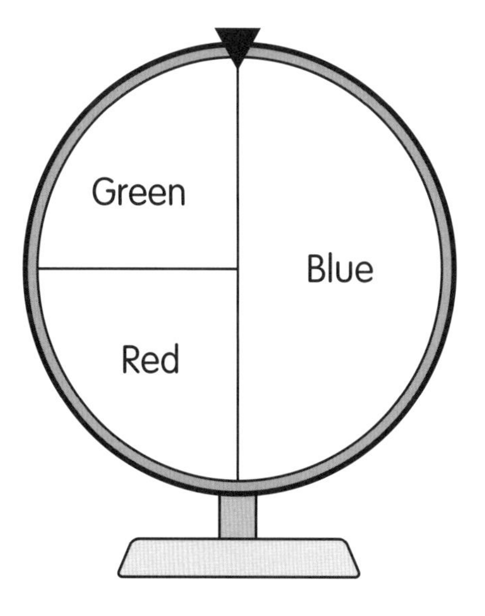

Who has made the most reasonable prediction?

Explain Your Thinking

Assessment of MATHEMATICS

Grade

3

1 There are 126 red balls, 214 green balls, and 98 balls in other colours in a box. How many balls are there in the box?

- ○ 186
- ○ 214
- ○ 242
- ○ 438

2 Which is the best estimate of the sum of the addition below?

```
    2 8 ◯
+ 1 ◯ 6
```

- ○ between 400 and 500
- ○ close to 500
- ○ less than 400
- ○ greater than 500

3 What number does the arrow point at on the number line below?

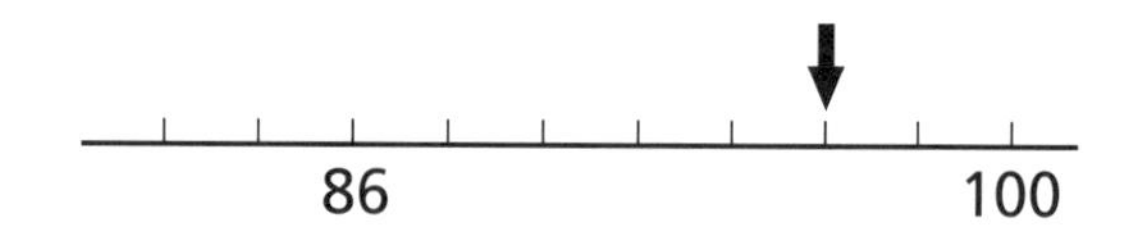

- ○ 91
- ○ 96
- ○ 98
- ○ 99

4 Lucy is making a gift box with the net below.

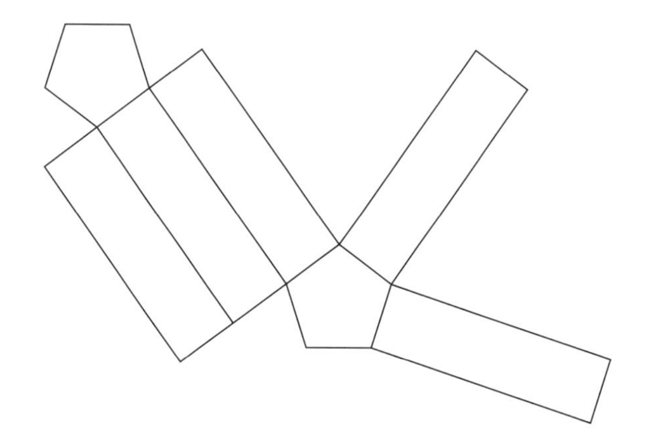

What is the figure of the gift box?

- ○ rectangular prism
- ○ pentagonal prism
- ○ rectangular pyramid
- ○ pentagonal pyramid

5 Julia has made a number pattern – add and then subtract. Which of the following could be Julia's pattern?

- O 13, 14, 16, 19, 23
- O 17, 20, 19, 22, 21
- O 20, 40, 60, 80, 100
- O 31, 26, 21, 16, 11

6 Look at the coins that Jason has.

If he pays the exact amount for a lollipop that costs $1.26 with the fewest coins, which coins will he have left?

- O 1 dime and 3 nickels
- O 1 quarter and 1 penny
- O 1 loonie and 1 penny
- O 1 quarter and 2 nickels

7 Kelvin is going to spin the spinner once.

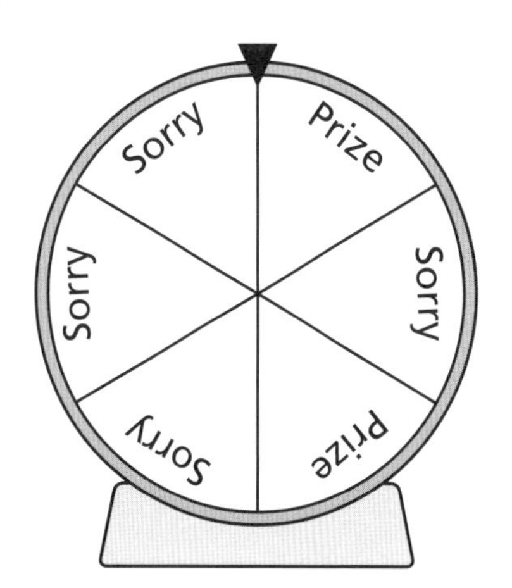

What is the probability that he will win a prize?

- O 2 out of 4
- O 2 out of 6
- O 6 out of 2
- O 4 out of 6

8 Tony is measuring his hand span. Which of the following could be the measurement of his hand span?

- O 13 mm
- O 11 m
- O 12 cm
- O 15 km

9 The flag is moved from M to N as shown on the grid below.

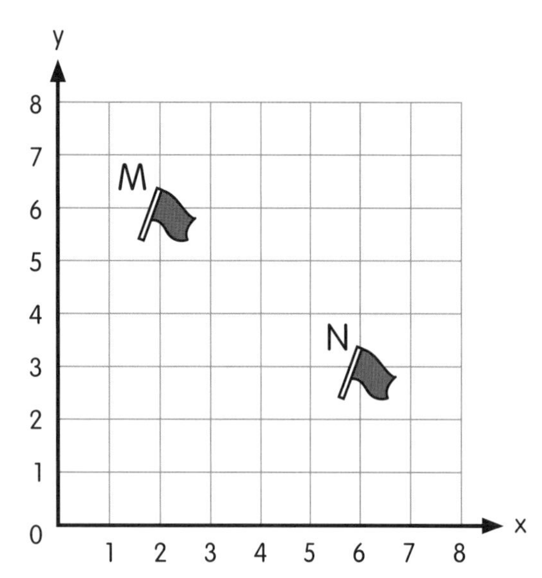

Which of the following describes the translation of the flag correctly?

- ○ 4 units left, then 3 units up
- ○ 3 units left, then 4 units up
- ○ 3 units right, then 4 units down
- ○ 4 units right, then 3 units down

10 Which subtraction sentence is related to 27 + 12 = 39?

- ○ 39 – 17 = 22
- ○ 39 – 12 = 27
- ○ 51 – 12 = 39
- ○ 27 – 12 = 15

11 Look at the points that Christine got in the first two rounds of a game.

Round	Score (points)
1st	124
2nd	98
3rd	

The score that Christine got in the 3rd round is 103 points fewer than the total score of the first two rounds. How many points did she get in the 3rd round?

- ○ 77
- ○ 119
- ○ 129
- ○ 325

12 It takes Sarah 69 days to make a doll. About how many weeks does it take her to make a doll?

- ○ 3
- ○ 6
- ○ 8
- ○ 10

13 Which of the following could be the temperature of a freezer?

- O 3°C
- O 36°C
- O –11°C
- O 98°C

14 The graph below shows the number of servings of fruit that each child eats in a week.

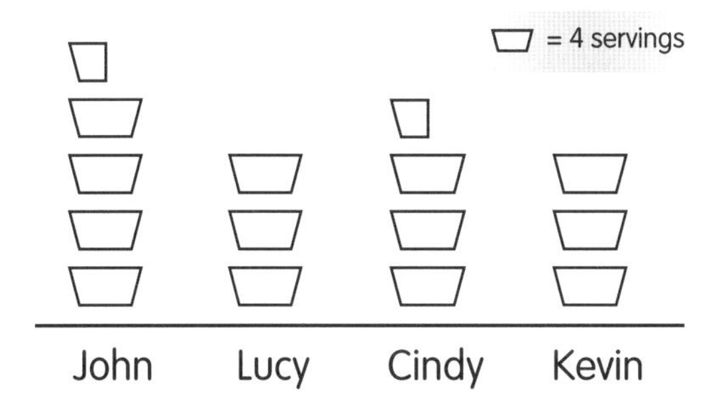

How many more servings of fruit do the boys have than the girls?

- O 1
- O 2
- O 4
- O 6

15 Which of the following sentence is true about a rectangular pyramid?

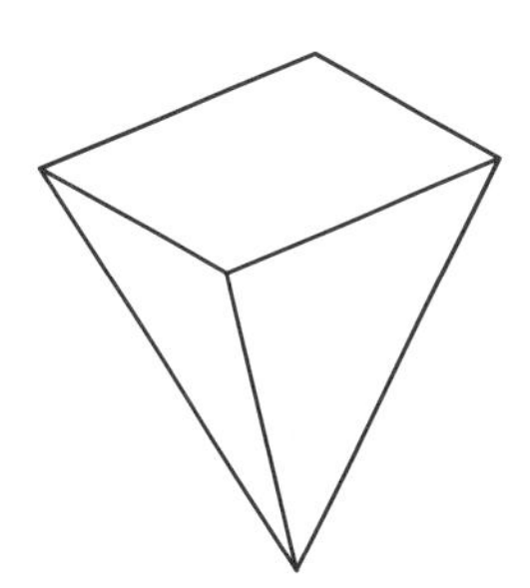

- O It has 5 edges.
- O It has 5 rectangular faces.
- O It has 8 vertices.
- O It has 4 triangular faces.

16 What is the missing number in the pattern below?

_____, 30, 46, 62, 78

- O 46
- O 26
- O 14
- O 12

17 Bernice has poured water into some glasses.

What fraction of the glasses is filled with water?

- O $\frac{2}{3}$
- O $\frac{2}{5}$
- O $\frac{3}{5}$
- O $\frac{4}{5}$

18 Michael wants to find the perimeter of a regular pentagon with a side length of 6 cm. Which number sentence should he use?

- O 5 x 5 x 5 x 5
- O 6 x 6 x 6 x 6 x 6
- O 5 + 5 + 5 + 5 + 5
- O 6 + 6 + 6 + 6 + 6

19 Which of the following slots is 248?

		A		B	C				D
240								256	

- O A
- O B
- O C
- O D

20 Which number are the sentences describing?

- It is an even number.
- It is divisible by 4.
- It is a multiple of 7.
- It is between 22 and 53.

- O 12
- O 28
- O 49
- O 56

21 Omar shares 42 gumballs equally with 6 of his cousins. How many gumballs does each person get?

- ○ 6
- ○ 7
- ○ 12
- ○ 14

22 The chart below shows the number of cans a family collected last week.

Day	Cans Collected
Mon	
Tue	
Wed	
Thu	
Fri	

= 4 cans

The number of cans collected on Friday doubled the number collected on Monday. How many cans should be drawn to complete the chart?

- ○ 2
- ○ 5
- ○ 10
- ○ 12

23 How many lines of symmetry are there in the shape below?

- ○ 2
- ○ 4
- ○ 6
- ○ 8

24 Daisy and Leo are building towers with blocks. The first tower is 2 blocks high, the second is 5 blocks high, the third is 8 blocks high and so on. How high will be the 7th tower?

- ○ 13
- ○ 15
- ○ 20
- ○ 23

25 Which of the following is the best measurement of the weight of a watermelon?

- O 200 g
- O 5 L
- O 6 kg
- O 3000 mL

26 Justin and Kelsey started their journey at 7:05 p.m. Justin arrived at the destination at 7:43 p.m. and Kelsey arrived 14 minutes later. What time did Kelsey arrive at the destination?

- O 7:19 p.m.
- O 7:29 p.m.
- O 7:57 p.m.
- O 8:14 p.m.

27 Look at Peter's design.

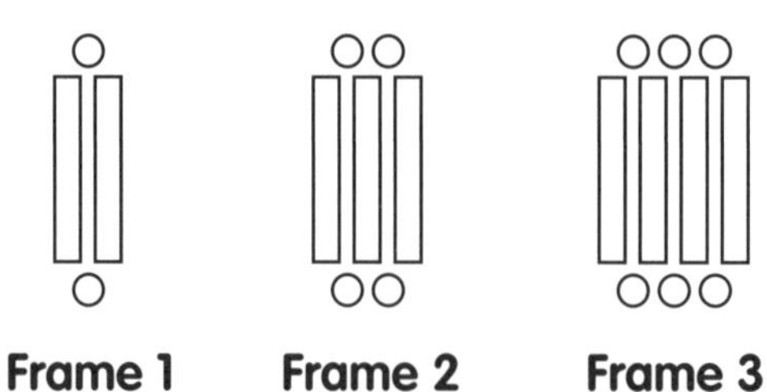

How many circles are there in the frame that has 6 rectangles?

- O 8
- O 10
- O 12
- O 14

28 How many nickels have the same value as the coins shown below?

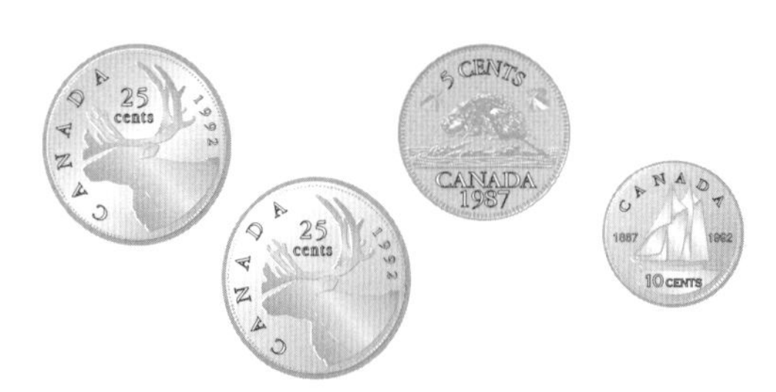

- O 6
- O 13
- O 40
- O 65

29 Mr. Green is drawing squares to make frames on his driveway using chalks. The number of squares and perimeter of each frame are recorded below.

Frame	Perimeter (Units)
	4
	6
	8
	10

What is the pattern rule for the perimeters?

If Mr. Green puts 5 pebbles in each square, what is the perimeter of the frame that has a total of 25 pebbles in it?

Explain Your Thinking

30 Sandra says, "I can build one prism and one pyramid with 6 pieces of modelling clay for each."

Do you think what Sandra says is possible?

Draw the figures to support your answer. Then describe the figures in terms of their edges and faces.

Show Your Work

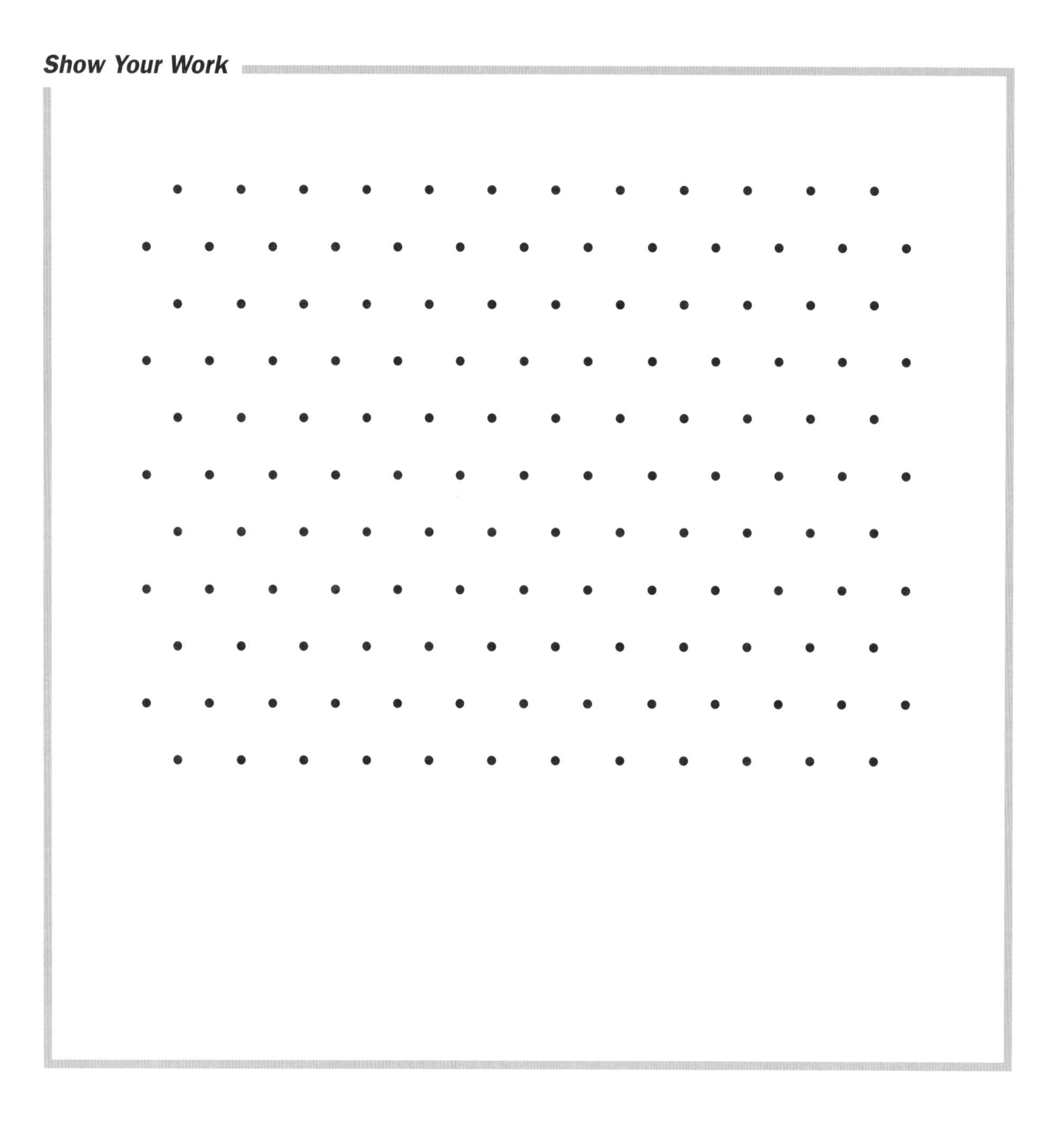

31 Jill did a survey on the number of hours her 22 friends spent watching TV in a week. She recorded the results in a tally chart.

Unfortunately, her cat tore a corner away.

Jill says, "I cannot make a bar graph to show the data anymore because there is some information missing."

Do you agree with Jill?

If not, explain and use the data to make a bar graph.

No. of Hours	Tally
10 or less	||
11	||||
12	𝍸
13	𝍸 |
14	

Explain Your Thinking

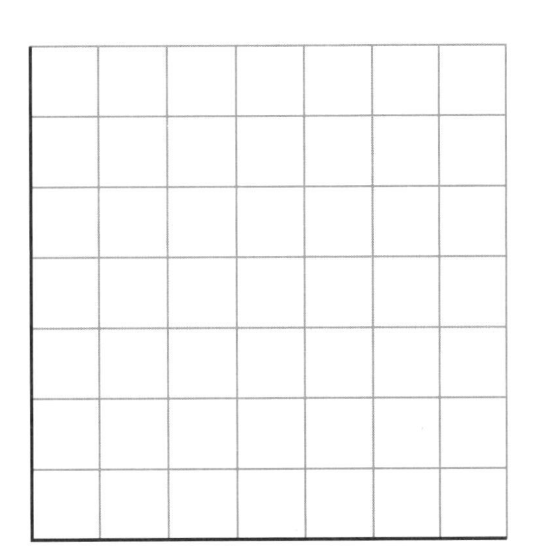

32 Carmen put 10 balls into the box and asked George to draw one without looking.

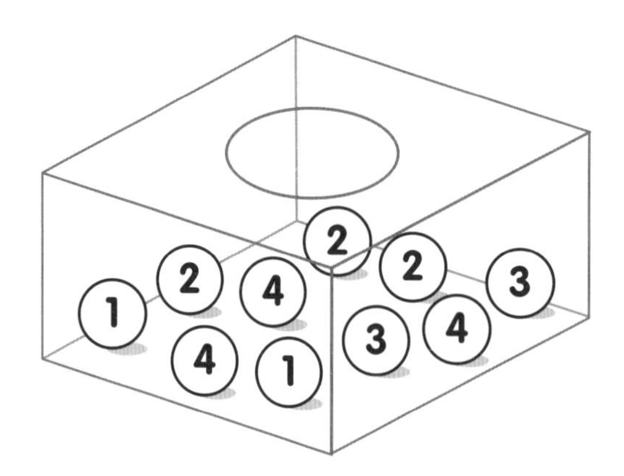

Carmen looked at the number on the ball that George drew and said, "The chance of drawing this ball is 3 out of 10."

Which number might be on the ball?

Explain Your Thinking

33 Steven and his sister want to buy a storybook which costs $8 for their brother.

The coins that each child has are as follows:

Steven: 4 loonies, 3 dimes, and 4 pennies

His sister: 2 toonies, 3 quarters, 4 dimes, and 3 nickels

If they chip in, will they be able to buy the storybook?

Explain Your Thinking

34 The areas of figure A and figure B are the same.

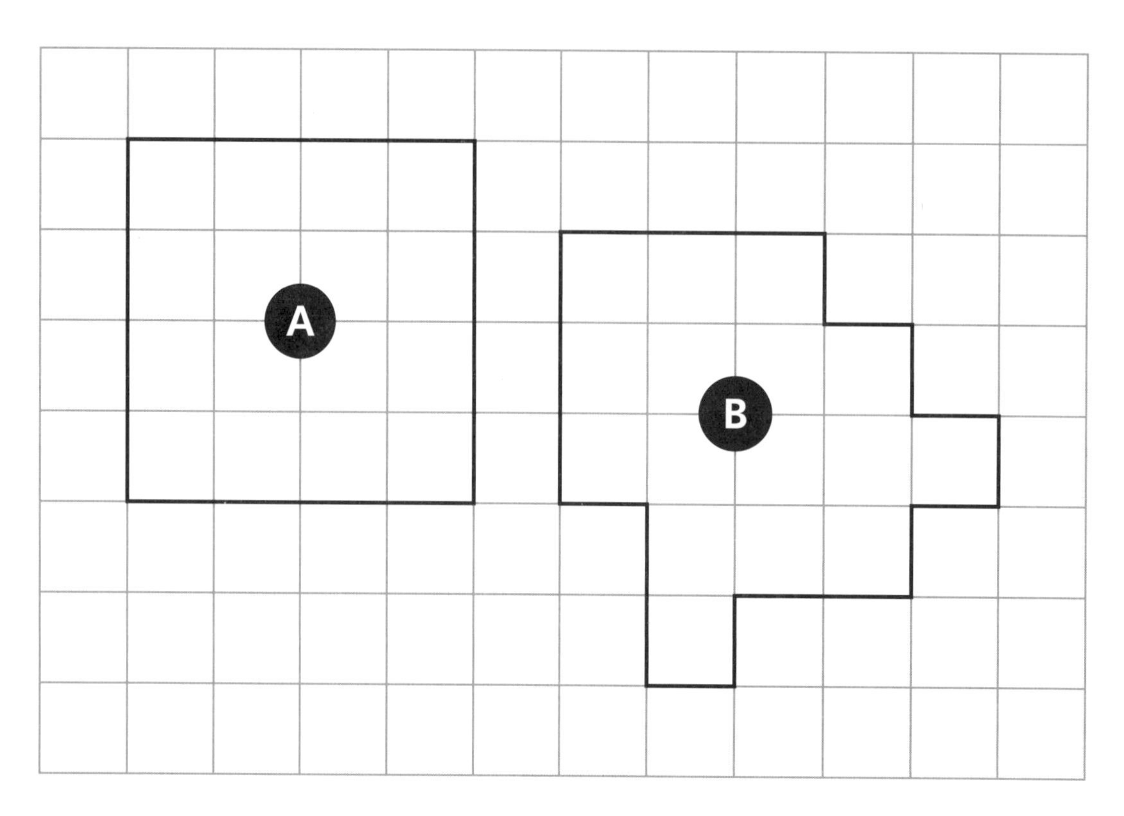

Jenny thinks that the perimeters of these two figures are the same too.

Do you agree? Give reasons to support your thinking.

Explain Your Thinking

35 Annie is making necklaces with red and blue beads. There are 9 beads on each necklace. The number of red beads on each necklace is 1 more than the blue ones.

How many red beads does she need to make 8 necklaces?

Show Your Work

36 You are treasure hunting.

What is the shortest and safest path to collect all the keys to the treasure chest?

You can move vertically or horizontally only.

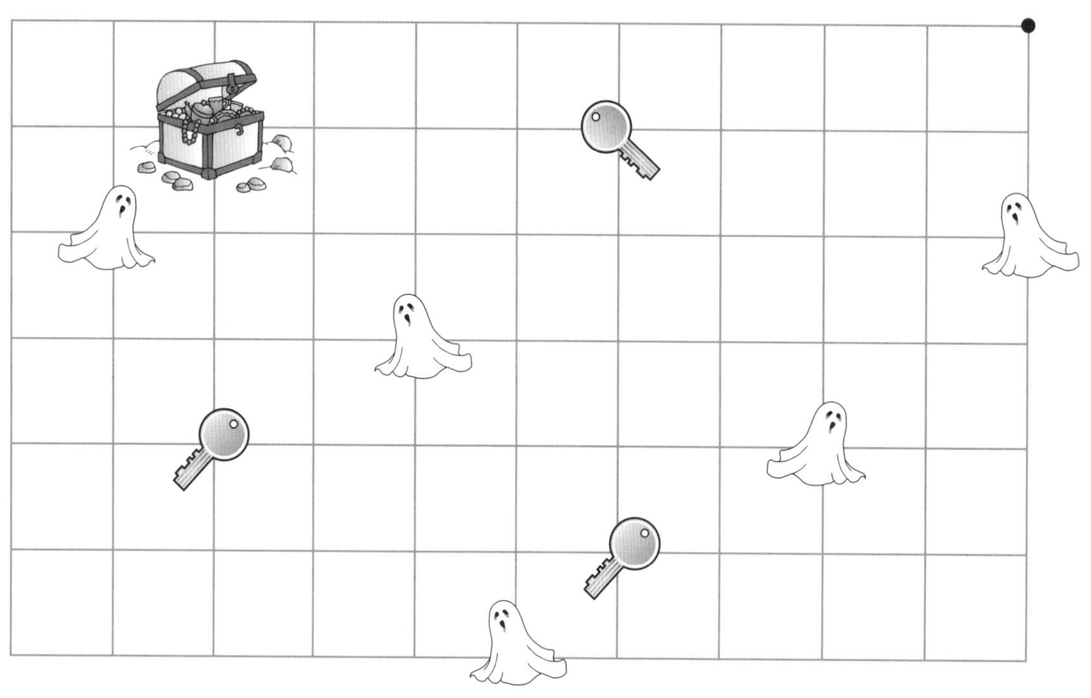

Show Your Work

Practice 1

1. 14
2. C
3. a bit shorter than 7 cm
4. rectangular prism
5. 7:15
6. 340 – 290
7. 16
8. unlikely
9. No. Andy has 28 stickers and Linda has 50. Linda has more stickers than Andy.
10.

Number of Apples	Number of Customers
1 – 5	𝍸
6 – 10	IIII
11 – 15	𝍸 III
16 – 20	𝍸
21 – 25	II

Most customers buy 11 – 15 apples.

Practice 2

1. 6:50 p.m.
2. 31 + 27 = 58
3. 429
4. rectangular pyramid
5. 7
6. 2
7. 88, 92
8. 398
9. 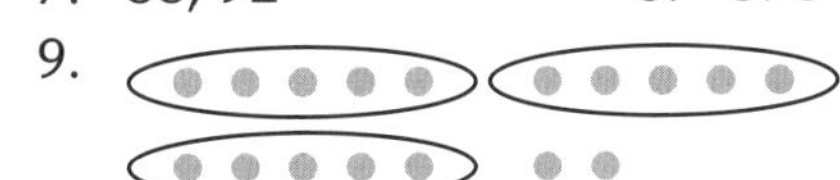
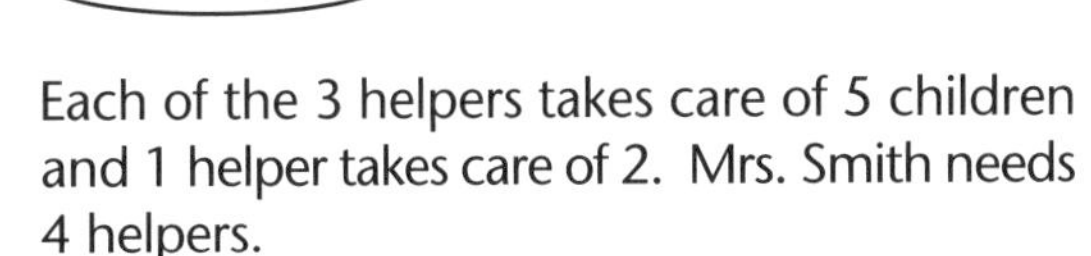
Each of the 3 helpers takes care of 5 children and 1 helper takes care of 2. Mrs. Smith needs 4 helpers.
10. Andrew misplaced the rectangular pyramid because it has 5 vertices instead of 6.

Practice 3

1. 24
2. 9
3.
4. 400 + 20 + 5
5. 8 ● and 4 □
6. about 30
7. likely
8. 10
9. I would use Way 1 because it is unlikely to draw a red ball, the prize of which costs the most, and it is most likely to draw a black ball, the prize of which costs least.
10. He will have the following coins left:

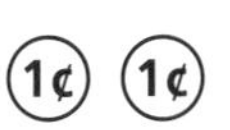

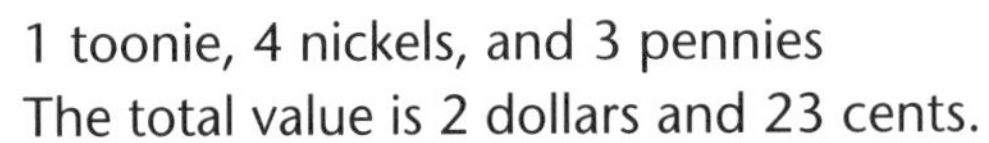
1 toonie, 4 nickels, and 3 pennies
The total value is 2 dollars and 23 cents.

Practice 4

1. 20 cm
2.
3. 5:20
4. a quarter
5. 629
6. 10
7. 24
8. 213
9. She bought a total of 36 lollipops. There are 9 lollipops in each bag.
10. Perimeter (units):
square: 12 ; rectangle: 14 ; L-shape: 14
Area (square units):
square: 9 ; rectangle: 10 ; L-shape: 8
He is not correct. The L-shape has the least area.

Practice 5

1.
2. 111
3. 36 – 28 = 8
4. 6
5. 7 km, 2600 m, 2 km, 300 cm
6. 7
7. 2
8. 75
9. 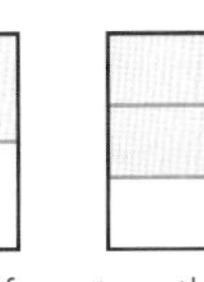
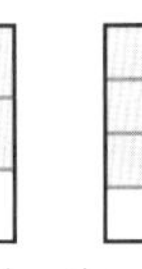
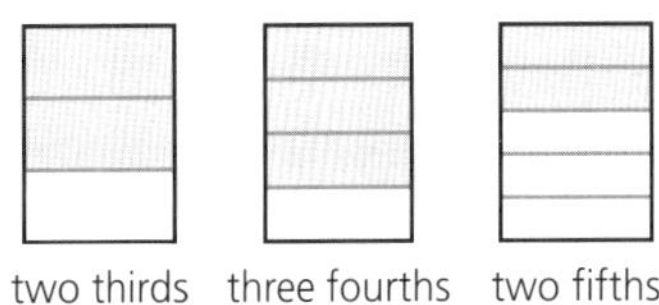
one half   two thirds   three fourths   two fifths
Least to greatest:
two fifths, one half, two thirds, three fourths
10. 

We can count 45 minutes backward to find the time that Danny started his dinner. The time was 6:25.

Practice 6

1. 2 km
2. 800 + 50 + 7
3. 4
4. 28 – 7 = 21
5. reflection
6. 10
7. 8:05 a.m.
8. line AB
9. 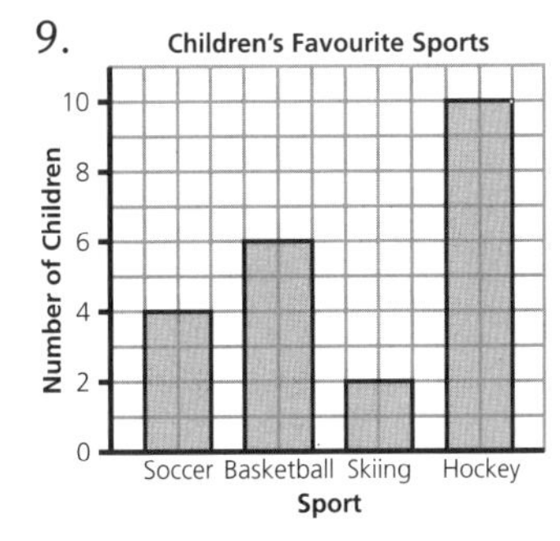

Mistakes:
- wrong title
- uneven scale
- uneven width of the bars

10. Annie should go 2 units right and 4 units down to get to the park. Then 2 units right and 2 units up to go back home.

Practice 7

1. Both have triangular faces.
2. 12
3. 25 x 250
4. 42
5. 283
6. unlikely
7. hexagonal pyramid
8. 8
9. Jack:

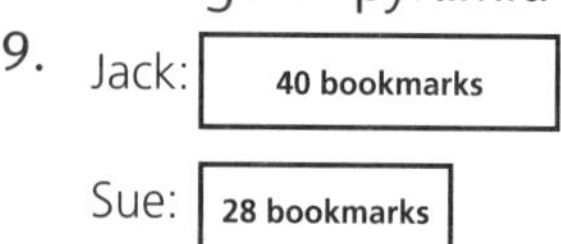

Difference: 12 bookmarks

Each shares: 12 ÷ 2 = 6
So, Jack should give 6 bookmarks to Sue.

10. **1** David→A→D→E→Jill 4
2 David→A→D→G→Jill 4
3 David→A→B→E→Jill 4
4 David→C→D→G→Jill 4
5 David→C→F→G→Jill 4
6 David→C→D→E→Jill 4
All the routes have the same distance.

Practice 8

1.
2. three quarters of a litre
3. 6
4. 40 cm
5. 2 units left, 3 units up
6. 16
7. about 1 year
8. Pattern rule: + 4, – 1
First pattern: 1, 5, 4, 8, 7
(Suggested answer for second pattern)
Second pattern: 10, 14, 13, 17
9.

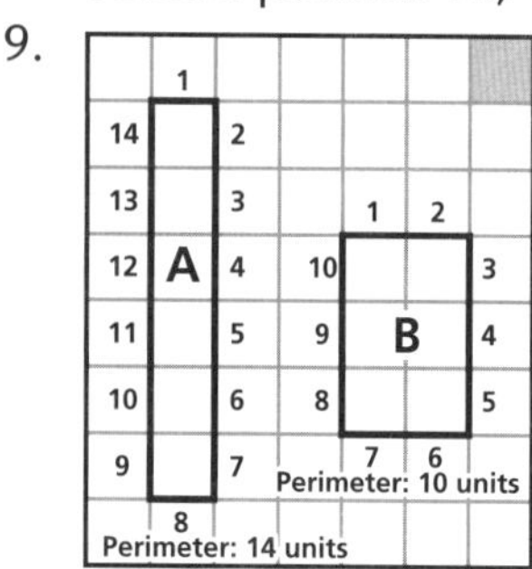

The flower bed with a smaller perimeter needs less fencing. She should choose B, which has the dimensions of 2 units by 3 units.

Practice 9

1. rectangular pyramid
2. 2 in 6
3. three fourths
4. 13
5. 22
6. 40 minutes
7. millimetres
8. 12
9. about 1 month
10. one third broken
one fourth for cookies
eggs left
Mrs. Green has 6 eggs left.
11.

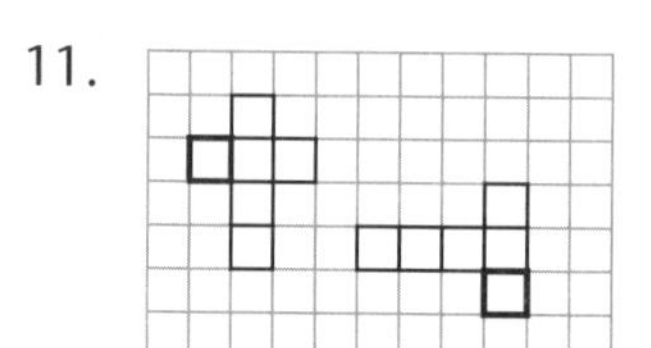

The nets can form cubes.

Practice 10

1. 2
2. 6
3. 6 km
4. She needs 5¢ more to get what she wants.
5. 24
6. 125
7. 13
8. C
9. Circle: 38 ; 47 ; 56 ; 65 ; 74 ; 83 ; 92
The numbers go down to the left diagonally. The digits in the tens columns increase by 1 each time, and the digits in the ones columns decrease by 1 each time.
10.

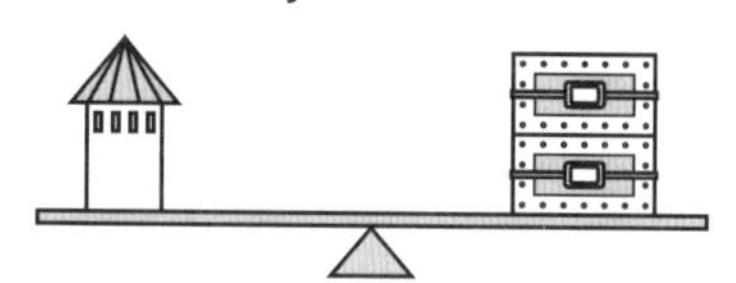

Two chests weigh 2 kg.

One tree and two cars weigh 2 kg in total.

Practice 11

1. 24
2. They have exactly one pair of equal angles.
3. 5 m, 9 m
4. 4 + 4 = 8

5. reflection
6. 1 L
7. July 6
8. 5
9.

Card Number	Tally
1	卌 II
2	卌 IIII
3	卌 卌 IIII

It is most likely to draw a "3" card and least likely to draw a "1" card. So the set of cards should have the most "3" cards and the least "1" cards. Janet might have set A.

10.

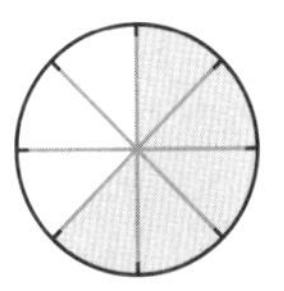

Pizza A

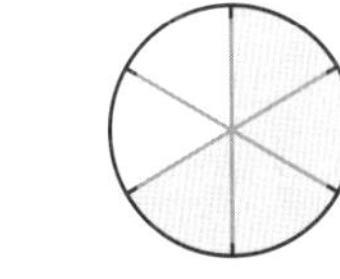

Pizza B

No, Uncle Sam is not correct, because four sixths is greater than five eighths as we can see in the diagrams.

Practice 12

1. 6 weeks
2. $42 \div 6 = 7$
3. $\frac{12}{20}$
4. 8
5. $\frac{4}{8}$
6. 2
7. likely
8. 10
9. Perimeter of the park: 500 (m)
   Total distance travelled: 500 x 3 = 1500 (m)
   So they will travel a total of 1500 m.
10.

Units	Triangles	Circles
1	2	3
2	4	6
3	6	9
4	8	12

Following the pattern, 6 units can be made with 12 triangles. Since there are 18 circles in 6 units, 18 circles are needed to go with 12 triangles.

Practice 13

1. It is equally likely to draw an odd number card or an even number card.
2. B, D, and E
3. 5 + 5 + 5
4. 114
5. add 3, subtract 1
6. POP
7. 20 cm

8. 30 ; 40 ; 20 ; 50

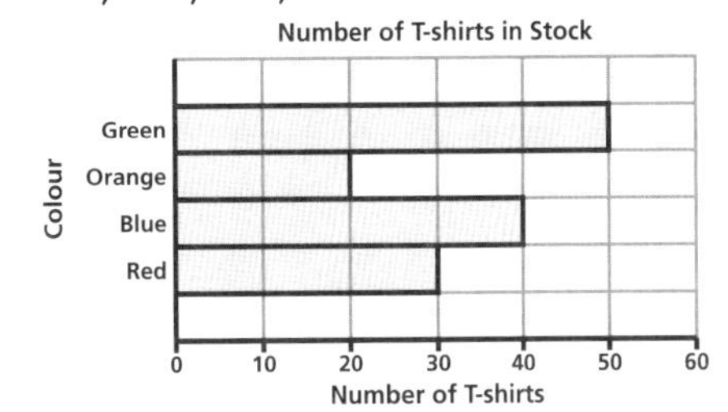

No, he should order orange T-shirts the most, because it has the highest sales figure.

9. (Suggested answers for examples)

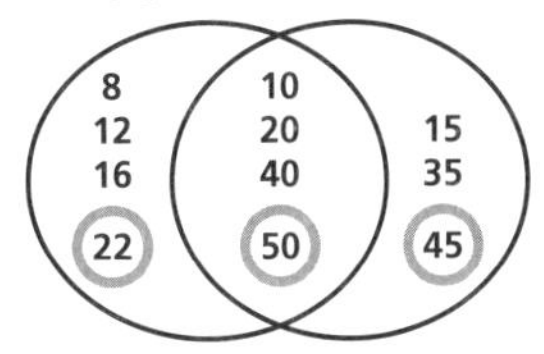

The numbers in the overlapping part are divisible by 2 and 5.

Practice 14

1. 2, 5, 11, 23, 47
2. rectangular faces and pyramids
3. 14
4. 15
5. 12:20 p.m.
6. The arrow makes a $\frac{1}{4}$ counterclockwise turn each time.
7. 4
8. 5
9.

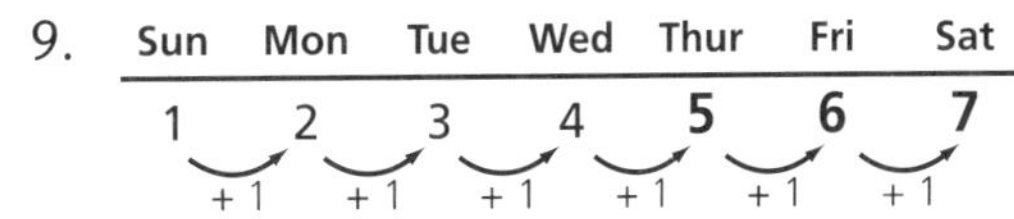

She will buy 5 bags of chips on Thursday, 6 bags on Friday and 7 bags on Saturday.
Total: 1 + 2 + 3 + 4 + 5 + 6 + 7 = 28 (bags)
She will buy 28 bags of chips in a week.

10. We expect the pointer to land on "blue" half of 60 times, which is 30 times. The number of times the pointer landing on "red" or "green" should be the same. Therefore, Brian's prediction is the most reasonable.

Assessment

1. 438
2. between 400 and 500
3. 96
4. pentagonal prism
5. 17, 20, 19, 22, 21
6. 1 dime and 3 nickels
7. 2 out of 6
8. 12 cm
9. 4 units right, then 3 units down
10. 39 – 12 = 27

11. 119
12. 10
13. –11°C
14. 4
15. It has 4 triangular faces.
16. 14
17. $\frac{3}{5}$
18. 6 + 6 + 6 + 6 + 6
19. B
20. 28
21. 6
22. 5
23. 4
24. 20
25. 6 kg
26. 7:57 p.m.
27. 10
28. 13
29. Pattern rule for perimeter:
    Start at 4. Add 2 each time.
    Pattern rule for number of pebbles:
    Start at 5. Add 5 each time.
    There are 25 pebbles in the frame that has 5 squares, and the perimeter of the frame is 12 units.
30.

Yes, it is possible. The figures are pentagonal pyramid and triangular prism. A pentagonal pyramid has 10 edges, 1 pentagon face, and 5 triangular faces. A triangular prism has 9 edges, 2 triangular faces, and 3 rectangular faces.

31.

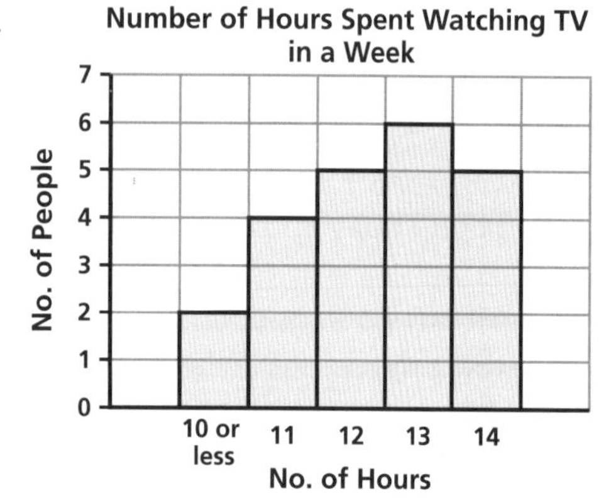

No, Jill is wrong. Since the number of people surveyed is 22, we can use subtraction to find the missing data. The missing data is 5 people.

32. There are 2 balls with a "1", 3 balls with a "2", 2 balls with a "3", and 3 balls with a "4". The probability of drawing a "1" is $\frac{2}{10}$, a "2" is $\frac{3}{10}$, a "3" is $\frac{2}{10}$, and a "4" is $\frac{3}{10}$.
    So, the number on the ball might be 2 or 4.

33. Steven has: 4 dollars and 34 cents
    Steven's sister has: 5 dollars and 30 cents
    Total: 9 dollars and 64 cents
    They are able to buy a storybook.
34. No, Jenny is wrong. The perimeter of figure A is 16 units, and the perimeter of figure B is 20 units.
35. There are 5 red beads and 4 blue beads in each necklace. 40 red beads are needed to make 8 necklaces.
36. (Suggested answer)
    1st key: 4 units left and 1 unit down
    2nd key: 4 units down
    3rd key: 4 units left and 1 unit up
    Chest: 3 units up